Having Nun, Partner?

David Bird

Finesse Bridge Publications

First published in the UK by Finesse Bridge Books Ltd 2000

ISBN 0 9538737 0 6

Distribution:

Worldwide (except USA): Central Books Ltd, 99 Wallis Road, London, E9 5LN.
Tel +44 (0)20 8986 4854.   Fax +44 (0)20 8533 5821.
E-mail orders@Centralbooks.com

USA: Baron Barclay Bridge Supplies, 3600 Chamberlain Lane #230, Louisville, KY40241, USA.   Web site http://www.baronbarclay.com
Tel 1-800-274-2221 (Toll free) or (502) 426 - 0410. Fax (502) 426 - 2044.

For all other enquiries, please contact the publishers, Finesse Bridge Books Ltd, 69 Masbro Road, Kensington, London W14 0LS.
Fax +44 (0)20 7371 1477. E-mail finesse@bcmchess.co.uk
Web site http://www.finessebooks.com

Typeset by Ruth Edmondson
Cover design by Ian Wileman, cartoon by Peter McClure
Printed in Great Britain by Redwood Books, Trowbridge, Wiltshire (UK).

Contents

The Players

The Convent first team

The Mother of Discipline   A grizzly 82-year-old nun, much feared by members of the novitiate.

Sister Grace   A strong player with a kindly nature, the Mother of Discipline's partner.

The Mother Superior   A sound player of placid disposition.

Sister Thomas   The novice mistress. A sour-faced, somewhat masculine nun.

Other Nuns

Sister Myrtle   An overweight nun, unaware of her total lack of ability at the game.

Sister Benedict   Sister Myrtle's equally talent-free partner.

The Novices

Sister Colleen   A fresh-faced Irish novice, showing considerable promise at the game.

Sister Carol   An attractive, blonde-haired novice, the partner of Sister Colleen.

Sister Theresa   Captain of judo at her secondary school and much admired in the novitiate.

Sister Perpetua   A very short girl, who has only recently learnt the game.

I

The Mother of Discipline's Remarkable Squeeze

It had been an unusually cold March and the blazing log fire in the convent cardroom was a necessity rather than a luxury.

'I've reserved Table 5 North-South for you, Reverend Mother,' said Sister Bernardine. 'Next to the fire is the place to be, I reckon, in this sort of weather.'

The Mother of Discipline had never seen such a strong fire. The occupants of Table 5 would surely be roasted alive by it. Table 6, the next one along, would be about right – warm enough, but not too much of a good thing. She adopted a pious expression. 'I don't like to take the best table by right,' she declared. 'Table 6 will be fine for Sister Thomas and myself.'

'I'm afraid Sister Euphemia and her partner are North-South at Table 6,' replied Sister Bernardine. 'As you see, we've already moved her wheelchair into place.'

'It's not set in concrete, is it?' snapped the Mother of Discipline. 'Get one of the novices to move her to Table 5.'

The Mother of Discipline shook her head sadly. 'No-one has any consideration nowadays,' she observed. 'You know what Sister Euphemia's circulation is like. She'll die of pneumonia if she's not right by the fire.'

Play started at the appointed hour of seven and the Mother of Discipline's first opponents were two of the less experienced novices.

Love All
Dealer East

```
                    ♠ A Q 8 4
                    ♥ 9 2
                    ♦ K J 9 4
                    ♣ 10 9 6
    ♠ 6 5 2                         ♠ 10 7 3
    ♥ 8 7 5 4          N            ♥ A
    ♦ 7 6 3         W     E         ♦ Q 10 8 2
    ♣ 8 4 2           S            ♣ A K Q J 3
                    ♠ K J 9
                    ♥ K Q J 10 6 3
                    ♦ A 5
                    ♣ 7 5
```

West	North	East	South
Sister	**Sister**	**Sister**	**Mother of**
Helena	**Thomas**	**Perpetua**	**Discipline**
-	-	1♣	2♥
pass	3♥	pass	4♥
all pass			

'Two Hearts was a weak jump overcall, was it?' enquired the fresh-faced Sister Helena.

'You know perfectly well that weak jump overcalls aren't allowed,' said the Mother of Discipline. 'It was an intermediate overcall, of course. Have you not read the late Terence Reese's opinion on the matter?'

'That was ages ago, Reverend Mother,' replied the novice. 'Most players in the novitiate reckon his views on bidding have gone out of date.'

'Oh, I *see*,' said the Mother of Discipline heavily. 'So, soundness has become an old-fashioned concept, has it? You'll be telling me next that safety plays are no longer fashionable.'

Sister Helena led ♣4 to her partner's ace and followed with ♣2 when the king was played. When the queen of clubs was led to the next trick, the Mother of Discipline turned towards the miniscule Sister Perpetua. 'What do you lead from three small?' she demanded.

'Three small what?' replied the novice uncertainly.

The Mother of Discipline gave a martyred sigh. 'Three small cards, what do you think?' she retorted. 'What would you lead from something like three cards to the eight, the top card or the middle card?'

'The top card, I expect,' replied Sister Perpetua. 'I don't really know. This is the first time I've played in a proper duplicate.'

'And which card on the second round?' persisted the Mother of Discipline.

The novice shrugged her shoulders. 'It wouldn't really matter if they were all small cards, would it?'

Giving up the struggle, the Mother of Discipline decided to ruff the third round of clubs high, with the king. Somewhat annoyed to see West follow suit, she then led a trump to dummy's nine. East won with the ace and played a fourth round of clubs, declarer ruffing with the queen. When East subsequently showed out on the second round of trumps the Mother of Discipline muttered something under her breath. West's ♡8 had been promoted into the setting trick and the game was one down.

The Mother of Discipline turned accusingly towards Sister Helena. 'What was this two of clubs on the second round?' she demanded. 'Were you trying to fool me?'

'No, indeed, Reverend Mother,' Sister Helena replied. 'With my regular partner I play that the second card in a suit is a suit preference signal. Here my diamonds were seven-high and the spades six-high. Not much in it really, but I decided to play the lower card.'

The bushy-eyebrowed Sister Thomas caught her partner's eye. 'Shouldn't you have crossed to dummy and led the two of trumps on the first round?' she said. 'You don't waste the nine, then.'

'Had I been properly informed of the opponents' signalling methods, I would have played the hand differently,' replied the Mother of Discipline.

It occurred to Sister Thomas that a high trump from the South hand would have been good enough too. If East won and persisted with a fourth round of clubs, declarer could ruff low. West would be welcome to overruff since she would be overruffed in turn by dummy's nine. Sister Thomas smiled to herself. It rather seemed that safety plays had become unfashionable.

A few rounds later one of the Convent's least able pairs arrived at the table, Sister Myrtle and Sister Benedict. Sister Myrtle had always been a large woman but following the demise of her recent 'fruit and juice' diet, she had gained weight at a frightening rate. She played the first board in Four Clubs, a favourite stopping place of hers. The scoresheet revealed that 3NT plus one had proved more popular elsewhere.

'Don't blame me,' exclaimed Sister Benedict. 'I could hardly risk 3NT with just four small spades in my hand.'

'I couldn't bid it either,' replied Sister Myrtle. 'I don't call three spades to the jack a reliable stopper, do you?'

'No, indeed,' said Sister Benedict. 'The hand was unbiddable, playing Acol.'

The Mother of Discipline was hoping for more of the same as she drew her cards for the second board of the round.

Game All
Dealer North

	♠ 8 5	
	♡ 7 2	
	◊ A 8 7 6 4 3 2	
	♣ 10 3	

♠ Q J 10 6 3		♠ 7 4 2
♡ A Q 10 5	N W E S	♡ J 9 8 6 3
◊ Q		◊ J 5
♣ Q J 5		♣ 9 8 4

	♠ A K 9	
	♡ K 4	
	◊ K 10 9	
	♣ A K 7 6 2	

West	North	East	South
Sister	**Sister**	**Sister**	**Mother of**
Myrtle	**Thomas**	**Benedict**	**Discipline**
-	pass	pass	2NT
pass	3NT	all pass	

Sister Myrtle led the queen of spades against 3NT and the Mother of Discipline won with the king. The problem on the hand was apparent to her – the diamond suit was blocked. She needed to duck the first or second round of diamonds, but if East gained the lead a heart switch would put the contract at risk. What could she do about it?

If West held the singleton queen of diamonds, a low diamond from hand would work well. West's queen would be allowed to win and the king of hearts would then be safe from attack. If instead West held any two or three cards in diamonds, playing the king first would work better. If West held honour doubleton, for example, she could be allowed to win the second round.

When the Mother of Discipline led the king of diamonds, the queen appeared from West and a small card from East. For a moment it was still possible that West had started with queen-jack doubleton in the diamond suit. This ray of hope was extinguished when Sister Myrtle rearranged her hand, standard practice when she had become void in a suit and wanted to reset to a black-red-black pattern.

The Mother of Discipline could see one more chance. If the spades were 5-3, she could exit with ace and another spade. When Sister Myrtle cashed her spade winners, one of declarer's diamonds could be discarded, leaving the diamond suit ready to run. Her mind made up, the Mother of Discipline cashed the ace of spades, then exited with ♠9. She breathed a sigh of relief when East produced a third spade.

Sister Myrtle won the third round of spades with the 10. Contrary to expectations, she did not cash her remaining two spades next. She switched to a low heart instead, East's jack drawing declarer's king. With the heart suit now bare, the Mother of Discipline had little alternative but to cash the eight tricks at her disposal. She conceded one down and turned scornfully towards Sister Myrtle. 'Why didn't you cash your two spade winners?' she demanded. 'Didn't you realise they were good?'

'I was fairly sure, yes,' replied Sister Myrtle. 'But you're such a strong player, I thought: if she wants me to cash them, perhaps I'd better not.'

Sister Thomas opened the scoresheet. 'Good gracious!' she exclaimed. 'Three pairs have bid and made Six Diamonds. 'No-one can have found the heart lead.'

Sister Myrtle reached for the North curtain card. 'You should open 3◊ with a seven-card suit,' she said. 'The Reverend Mother bids Blackwood and you're in the slam.'

'I know a vulnerable pre-empt when I see one,' declared Sister Thomas. 'Ace-empty to seven and three small doubletons is not one of them.' She filled in the scoresheet, in a near illegible scribble, and thrust it back into the board. Three Diamonds, indeed! If she needed any lectures on bidding from the worst player in the Convent, she would ask for them.

'One ace is all the Mother of Discipline needs,' said Sister Myrtle.

Play continued and the next round brought the Convent's two top pairs face to face.

North-South Game
Dealer North

```
              ♠ K 10 3
              ♡ A K 6 5 2
              ◊ 5 2
              ♣ K 9 4
♠ 6 5                          ♠ 8 4
♡ J 10 9 7 3       N           ♡ 8
◊ Q 9 4        W       E       ◊ K J 10 8 7 6
♣ Q J 5            S           ♣ 10 7 6 2
              ♠ A Q J 9 7 2
              ♡ Q 4
              ◊ A 3
              ♣ A 8 3
```

West	North	East	South
Mother	**Sister**	**Sister**	**Mother of**
Superior	**Thomas**	**Grace**	**Discipline**
-	1♡	pass	2♠
pass	3♠	pass	4♣
pass	4♡	pass	5◊
pass	5♡	pass	7♠
all pass			

Spades were agreed as trumps at an early stage. When Sister Thomas cue-bid the ace and king of hearts, the Mother of Discipline could see there would be play for a grand slam. Six spade tricks, five heart tricks and two minor-suit aces would bring the total to thirteen. 'Seven Spades,' she said.

A trump was led and the Mother of Discipline nodded happily as she inspected the dummy. There were twelve tricks on top and unless the heart division was particularly unfriendly a thirteenth trick could be ruffed good in that suit. She drew trumps in two rounds, then played the queen and ace of hearts. She could not believe it when East showed out on the second round. 'That's been the story of our evening', she said, slumping back in her chair.

The only remaining chance was to run the trump suit, hoping for some miracle to occur. When trump after trump appeared from the South hand, the Mother Superior had some awkward discards to find. Since she held the sole heart guard, she was forced to abandon one of the minors. She decided to unguard the diamonds and this end position arose:

Sr. Thomas
♠ —
♡ K 6
◇ 5
♣ K 9

M. Superior
♠ —
♡ 10 9
◇ —
♣ Q J 5

Sr. Grace
♠ —
♡ —
◇ K J
♣ 10 7 6

M. of Discipline
♠ —
♡ —
◇ A 3
♣ A 8 3

When the Mother of Discipline led ◇A from her hand, West had to throw a club, retaining her heart guard. Declarer crossed to the club king and cashed the king of hearts. Sister Grace had to throw a club too, to retain her diamond guard. The Mother of Discipline discarded her ◇3. Somewhat flushed by her exertions, she then claimed the last two tricks with her ♣A8. 'A compound squeeze, as I live and breathe,' she declared.

The Mother Superior smiled at her colleague. 'You timed it excellently,' she said.

Sister Thomas looked disdainfully at the scoresheet. 'We'd have scored above average for bidding and making *Six* Spades,' she reported. 'Appalling standard of bidding.'

The bells of the extern chapel were sounding ten o'clock as the last round began. The two novices at the Mother of Discipline's table gathered their concentration. It mattered little to them what results they obtained. The main objective was to avoid any appearance of the MD's punishment book.

The first board passed by satisfactorily from the novices' point of view, the Mother of Discipline scoring a joint top in Four Spades. This was the last deal of the evening:

Game All   ♠ J 9 3
Dealer North   ♥ A J 2
                            ◇ A K 5
                            ♣ A J 7 4

♠ K 4   ♠ A Q 8 7 2
♥ Q 9 8 7 3   N   ♥ 6
◇ J 6 3 2   W   E   ◇ 10 9 8
♣ K 6   S   ♣ Q 10 9 3

                            ♠ 10 6 5
                            ♥ K 10 5 4
                            ◇ Q 7 4
                            ♣ 8 5 2

West	North	East	South
Sister	**Sister**	**Mother of**	**Sister**
Thomas	**Carol**	**Discipline**	**Colleen**
-	1♣	1♠	pass
pass	double	pass	2♥
double	all pass		

Sister Colleen, a pale-faced novice from County Cork, had a close decision on the second round of the auction. Should she bid 2♣ or 2♥? Partner's re-opening double suggested four cards in hearts and she opted eventually for the higher-scoring contract.

Sister Colleen regretted her decision when she heard a sharp double on her left. There was no further bidding and West led the king of spades. The defenders scored three tricks in the suit, Sister Thomas discarding a diamond on the third round. Declarer won the diamond switch with the queen and took a successful finesse of dummy's jack of trumps. The ace of trumps brought less good news, East showing out.

Sister Colleen looked apologetically at her partner. It seemed that she would lose two club tricks and two trump tricks, in addition to the three spade tricks already lost. 'Sorry, partner,' she said. 'I'm afraid this is going to be a bad one.'

Two more diamond winners stood up, leaving this end position:

Sr. Carol
♠ —
♡ 2
◊ —
♣ A J 7 4

Sr. Thomas
♠ —
♡ Q 9 8
◊ —
♣ K 6

M. of Discipline
♠ 8
♡ —
◊ —
♣ Q 10 9 3

Sr. Colleen
♠ —
♡ K 10
◊ —
♣ 8 5 2

'Ace of clubs, please,' said Sister Colleen.

Sister Thomas peered down her nose at this card, eventually unblocking the club king. It brought her little relief. Declarer exited with a club, won by East's 10. When the Mother of Discipline played another club winner, Sister Thomas had to ruff her partner's trick. The trump return into South's tenace gave the young declarer the last two tricks and the contract was made.

'Bad luck, partner,' said Sister Carol. 'Most unfortunate trump break. How many down were you?'

Sister Colleen was unsure of the correct etiquette in this situation. It was surely against Convent regulations to make a doubled contract against the Mother of Discipline. 'I lost count of the tricks,' she replied. 'One down, was it, Reverend Mother?'

'There are many unscrupulous characters in this world who would take advantage of a concession like that,' replied the Mother of Discipline. 'You made eight tricks. That's plus 670.'

Sister Carol opened the scoresheet and wrote down the score in the laborious copperplate handwriting that was compulsory for members of the novitiate. 'It's quite a good one for us,' she announced.

'I don't think my double can be faulted, Reverend Mother,' said Sister Thomas stiffly. 'I had to try for the 200 and you had very little for your overcall. How many points did you have, in fact?'

13

'Points?' exclaimed the Mother of Discipline. 'What relevance are points when you have a chance to call One Spade over One Club?'

A subdued Sister Thomas sat back in her chair. 'Minus 110 would have been bad for us anyway,' she said.

'There was nothing wrong with the bidding,' declared the Mother of Discipline. 'It was the defence that went wrong. When you ruffed my queen of clubs you had to give them a trick with your return.'

Sister Thomas gritted her teeth. It was typical of the MD to state the blindingly obvious. What alternative to ruffing was there when you had nothing but trumps in your hand?

'You ruffed the wrong winner,' continued the Mother of Discipline. 'You should have ruffed my ace of spades at Trick 3! Then you can exit peacefully and still come to your queen of trumps in the endgame.'

The Mother of Discipline turned towards Sister Colleen. 'Do you follow what I'm talking about?' she said. 'Sister Thomas was blessed with the opportunity to make an extremely rare play – a Grand Coup by a defender at Trick 3.'

'Yes, I see, Reverend Mother,' replied Sister Colleen, who had not understood one word of the analysis.

The Mother of Discipline looked severely across the table. 'There you are,' she said. 'It was obvious to the merest novice!'

II

Sister Colleen's Penance

Sister Colleen could feel her heart pounding as she stood before the door marked 'Mother of Discipline'. The evil moment could be postponed no longer and she knocked on the door.

'Enter!' called a harsh voice from within.

Sister Colleen entered the room and bowed her head as a mark of respect. 'I was sent to you by Sister Thomas, Reverend Mother,' she said. 'I'm ashamed to report that I opened an 11-point hand in last night's pairs.'

The Mother of Discipline, who was seated behind a large desk, glared at the novice. 'Presumably you're aware of the rule that novices may not open on fewer than twelve points?'

'Yes, Reverend Mother, but I was in the third seat and I held six hearts to the...'

'Be silent!' cried the Mother of Discipline. 'You youngsters today don't realise how lucky you are. When I first joined St Hilda's, novices were required to hold a full 14 points before opening the bidding.'

'Didn't that result in a lot of missed games, Reverend Mother?'

'What on earth do missed games matter?' continued the ancient nun, unscrewing her fountain pen. 'It taught us that the Convent rules had been fashioned for our own good and were to be obeyed without question. Do you hear me? Without question.'

'Yes, Reverend Mother.'

'You know the story of St John the Dwarf?' continued the Mother of Discipline, peering over her spectacles. 'When he was a novice he was ordered to water a dead stick every day. He did so, under obedience, and in the third year the stick brought forth fruit. What did it do?'

'It brought forth fruit, Reverend Mother.'

The Mother of Discipline reached for her Punishment Book. 'As a penance for your lack of respect you will score all the Convent duplicates for the next two months... ah no, I see I've already allocated that to Sister Ambrosine.'

Sister Colleen stood patiently to attention, waiting to hear her fate. So, the MD had found out about Sister Ambrosine's Unusual Notrump bid the other day. The walls certainly seemed to have ears in this establishment.

'Let's keep it simple,' declared the Mother of Discipline, scratching an entry in her punishment book. 'Three days on Saint Iona's regime.'

Sister Colleen looked puzzled. 'Saint Iona's regime?' she said. 'I don't know what that is, Reverend Mother.'

The Mother of Discipline sighed heavily. 'It means that you eat your morning cereal without any milk, you maintain a total silence between Lauds and mid-day, and you sleep without a pillow.'

Sister Colleen could not believe what she was hearing. A penance like that, just for a light opening bid!

'There's no need to adopt that lofty expression,' reprimanded the Mother of Discipline. 'Our beloved Saint Iona passed her whole life under such a regime. A splendid example to us all.'

Sister Colleen headed for the novitiate cardroom, where the novices' practice duplicate was about to take place.

'Take your seats, girls!' cried Sister Thomas, the novice mistress whose task it was to run such events. 'Remember to be friendly and gracious to each other at all times.'

The game started and on the first board Sister Colleen picked up this hand:

> ♠ A 7 6 5 3
> ♡ 8 2
> ◇ K 8 2
> ♣ A 7 3

The first two players passed and Sister Colleen thumbed through her cards uncertainly. It was a totally obvious One Spade opening in the third seat but the MD would go berserk if she heard of it so soon after the other offence. Still, Sister Thomas was at the far side of the room. No-one would ever find out. 'One Spade,' said Sister Colleen.

The auction continued and a few seconds later the novice found herself in Four Spades doubled. This was the full deal:

```
Love All              ♠ Q 9 8 2
Dealer North          ♡ A Q 5 3
                      ◇ 10 4
                      ♣ J 6 4
    ♠ K J                              ♠ 10 4
    ♡ K J 7 4           N              ♡ 10 9 6
    ◇ A Q 9         W       E          ◇ J 7 6 5 3
    ♣ K Q 10 5          S              ♣ 9 8 2
                      ♠ A 7 6 5 3
                      ♡ 8 2
                      ◇ K 8 2
                      ♣ A 7 3
```

West	North	East	South
Sister	**Sister**	**Sister**	**Sister**
Ambrosine	**Carol**	**Perpetua**	**Colleen**
-	pass	pass	1♠
double	4♠	pass	pass
double	all pass		

The dark-haired Sister Ambrosine led the king of clubs against Four Spades doubled, wincing as the jack appeared in the dummy. Sister Colleen surveyed the limited assets at her disposal. How on earth could she make ten tricks?

'What contract are you in?' boomed a deep voice from behind Sister Colleen.

Sister Colleen froze in her seat. 'Er... Four Spades doubled, Sister,' she replied.

'That's much too high,' continued Sister Thomas. 'What was the auction?'

'I can't remember, Sister,' declared Sister Colleen.

Sister Ambrosine leaned forward helpfully. 'It was One Spade from South, I doubled and North raised to Four Spades,' she said. 'When that ran back to me I doubled again.'

Sister Colleen could barely tolerate the suspense as Sister Thomas digested this auction. She would surely be reported for her light opening bid and the consequences did not bear thinking about.

'The Lord preserve us from such bidding!' exclaimed Sister Thomas. 'A raise to Four Spades was far too much on the North hand.'

Sister Carol was surprised to hear this. 'I would have bid Three without the double, Sister,' she said. 'The Mother of Discipline told us we had to bid one more than normal over a double.'

'That doesn't apply at the four level,' declared Sister Thomas. 'If you thought you were worth a double raise, which you're not, you should have bid 2NT over the double.'

Sister Colleen won the first trick with the ace of clubs and finessed the queen of hearts successfully. She cashed the ace of hearts and ruffed a heart, Sister Ambrosine dropping a mildly deceptive king. The young declarer, who had noted East's ♣2 at Trick 1, now judged it was safe to play a second round of clubs. West rose with the queen and exited with a third round of clubs.

Sister Colleen was now at the crossroads. Where was the last heart? If East held it, she should go for the endplay immediately, playing ace and another trump. If West had it, she should ruff another heart first, to remove West's safe exit card.

'Come on, come on,' said Sister Thomas. 'Don't spend all afternoon on it.'

Eventually Sister Colleen decided to play West for the last heart. If she did hold only three hearts the contract would still be made if her shape was 1-3-5-4 and she had to ruff with the bare king.

As it happened, it was East who showed out on the fourth round of hearts. Sister Colleen ruffed in the South hand, then played ace and another trump. West won with the trump king and had no good return. A club would concede a ruff-and-discard, so she had to play ace and another diamond. Declarer produced the diamond king and ten tricks had been made.

Sister Ambrosine, who was fuming inwardly, managed to contort her face into a smile. 'Beautifully played, indeed, Sister Colleen,' she said.

Sister Thomas nodded approvingly. The defenders had missed a good three chances to break the contract but it had still been an excellent effort by the young declarer.

'Your double was very unlucky,' replied Sister Colleen. 'It was such a fine double, it deserved a top.'

Sister Thomas moved away to another table and the four novices exhaled simultaneously, glad to have survived the experience. 'You lucky devil!' exclaimed Sister Ambrosine. 'Eleven points opposite nine? You needed a year's worth of luck to bring that one home.'

Sister Colleen nodded, rubbing her hands together gleefully. '590 to the good guys!' she exclaimed.

This was the second board of the round:

Love All
Dealer West

	♠ A 4 2	
	♡ J 10 6 5 4	
	◊ Q 5	
	♣ A K 4	
♠ J 6 3		♠ K
♡ Q 8 7 3		♡ 9 2
◊ 7 2		◊ A K 10 9 6 4
♣ 10 8 7 2		♣ J 9 6 3
	♠ Q 10 9 8 7 5	
	♡ A K	
	◊ J 8 3	
	♣ Q 5	

West	North	East	South
Sister	**Sister**	**Sister**	**Sister**
Ambrosine	**Carol**	**Perpetua**	**Colleen**
pass	1♡	2◊	2♠
pass	3♠	pass	4♠
all pass			

Sister Colleen arrived in Four Spades and West led ◊7. Sister Perpetua, a tiny girl whose head was barely above the level of the table, cashed two rounds of diamonds, then paused for thought. How about playing a third round of diamonds? If West could insert some trump higher than dummy's four, the ace would be forced. Yes, then her king would make a trick!

Sister Perpetua continued with the ten of diamonds, West ruffing with the six. Sister Colleen overruffed with dummy's ace and called for a trump. East's king won the trick and a further round of diamonds promoted West's bare jack of trumps. The game was one down.

Sister Ambrosine smiled to herself. 'Fancy losing two trump tricks with a holding like that,' she said.

Sister Colleen looked round to check that Sister Thomas was nowhere nearby. 'Oh, so I suppose you wouldn't have done, then?' she replied.

'What if you don't overruff the six?' continued Sister Ambrosine. 'You win my return and play the ace of trumps, dropping the king. The queen drops the jack on the next round and you make it.'

'Double-dummy play,' retorted Sister Colleen. 'It was cold on my line, unless East held a singleton king.'

'Even that isn't true,' persisted Sister Ambrosine. 'Suppose East started with king or jack doubleton. When you overruff and lead a trump from dummy, a small card appears from East. You'd have to guess which honour to play.'

A round or two later, Sister Colleen and her partner faced two novices who had little interest in bridge and played the game only under protest. Sister Colleen reached an eccentric contract on the first board of the round:

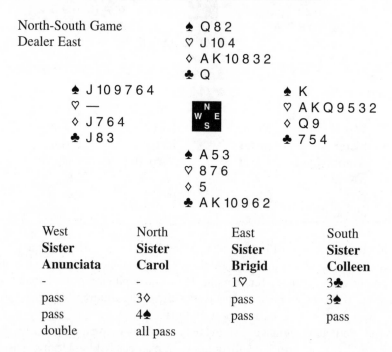

North-South Game
Dealer East

```
              ♠ Q 8 2
              ♡ J 10 4
              ◇ A K 10 8 3 2
              ♣ Q

♠ J 10 9 7 6 4              ♠ K
♡ —                         ♡ A K Q 9 5 3 2
◇ J 7 6 4          N        ◇ Q 9
♣ J 8 3         W     E     ♣ 7 5 4
                   S
              ♠ A 5 3
              ♡ 8 7 6
              ◇ 5
              ♣ A K 10 9 6 2
```

West	North	East	South
Sister	**Sister**	**Sister**	**Sister**
Anunciata	**Carol**	**Brigid**	**Colleen**
-	-	1♡	3♣
pass	3◇	pass	3♠
pass	4♠	pass	pass
double	all pass		

The jack of trumps was led and down went the dummy. 'Are you out of your mind, Carol?' demanded Sister Colleen. 'My 3♠ bid was looking for notrumps. How can you raise with only three trumps?'

'What else could I do?' her partner replied.

Sister Colleen played low from dummy on the trump lead and captured East's king with the ace. She cashed two diamond winners, throwing a heart, then ruffed a diamond in hand. A club to the queen allowed her to ruff dummy's last diamond, West following suit. Two more rounds of clubs stood up and this position had been reached:

Sr. Carol
♠ Q 8
♡ J
◊ 10 8
♣ —

Sr. Anunciata
♠ 10 9 7 6 4
♡ —
◊ —
♣ —

Sr. Brigid
♠ —
♡ A K Q 5 3
◊ —
♣ —

Sr. Colleen
♠ —
♡ 8 7
◊ —
♣ 10 9 6

Declarer had scored the first eight tricks. When she led a club, West ruffed with the nine and a heart was thrown from dummy. 'I must make the queen and eight of trumps now,' declared Sister Colleen. 'Ten tricks.'

'That was rather lucky,' observed Sister Brigid. 'You had three heart losers off the top and you were missing K-J-10-9 to seven trumps.'

'It was the only makeable game,' Sister Colleen replied. 'We can't make 3NT, even with the void heart on lead and the clubs breaking 3-3. A spade lead knocks out the entry to the clubs.'

'That's right,' said an amused Sister Carol. 'You can't let East's king of spades win the first trick. She would cash the heart suit.'

'Bridge is a silly game and that was a stupid hand,' declared the pale-faced Sister Anunciata. 'Just think how much work I could be doing if I wasn't wasting my time here.'

On the next round Sister Colleen faced a minor rival of hers, Sister Theresa. Gleaming with health, a former captain of judo at her secondary school, Sister Theresa was a much admired figure in the novitiate.

This was the first board they played:

```
North-South Game          ♠ A 4
Dealer West               ♡ 8 7 3
                          ◇ 10 9 7 3
                          ♣ 8 4 3 2

    ♠ Q 10 7                           ♠ J 8 6 3 2
    ♡ 9 4              N               ♡ 10 6 2
    ◇ Q 8 6 5 4 2    W   E             ◇ J
    ♣ 7 5              S               ♣ A K 9 6

                          ♠ K 9 5
                          ♡ A K Q J 5
                          ◇ A K
                          ♣ Q J 10
```

West	North	East	South
Sister	**Sister**	**Sister**	**Sister**
Katherine	**Carol**	**Theresa**	**Colleen**
pass	pass	pass	2♣
pass	2◇	pass	2NT
pass	3♣	double	3♡
pass	4♡	all pass	

Sister Colleen ended in Four Hearts after a five-card Stayman sequence. Sister Katherine, a shy girl who had not been blessed with the best of complexions, led ♣7 in response to her partner's lead-directing double. East scored two tricks in the suit and continued with a third round. Sister Katherine ruffed in the West seat, then played a diamond to the jack and ace.

Sister Colleen surveyed the scene with a pained expression. That club lead was bad luck. How many other novices would find Theresa's double of Three Clubs? Indeed, how many other North-South pairs were playing five-card Stayman? Most of them would be in an easy 3NT, maybe scoring an overtrick. Still, the priority now was to make sure of ten tricks in the heart game. The only risk seemed to be an overruff in spades. If the remaining trumps were 2-2, a couple of rounds of trumps before taking the ruff would guarantee the contract.

Sister Colleen drew two rounds of trumps, West showing out on the second round. With one trump still out, she then took her spade ruff. This passed by successfully but when she tried to return to hand with a diamond East struck with her last trump. The game was one down.

Sister Theresa gazed triumphantly at her opponent. 'You shouldn't draw those trumps,' she declared. 'You can get back to hand with a trump, then.'

'What rubbish you talk!' exclaimed Sister Colleen. 'T'was a fine safety play, I made there. It was no justice at all that diamonds were 6-1.'

'What do you mean, safety play?' persisted Sister Theresa. 'You mean you were guarding against a 6-2 spade break?'

'Ah, you've spotted it now,' said Sister Colleen. 'Well done.'

'Spades couldn't be 6-2,' declared Sister Theresa. 'If either of us held six spades we'd have opened a Multi.'

A black shape appeared at the table. 'Are you having an argument, girls?' demanded Sister Thomas.

'No, indeed, Sister,' replied Sister Theresa. 'I was just congratulating the declarer on her excellent safety play.'

'It didn't sound like it to me,' reprimanded Sister Thomas. 'Any further poor behaviour and you'll be reporting yourselves to the Mother of Discipline.'

'I've rarely seen a better played hand,' said Sister Theresa, raising her voice so that the words might catch the departing Sister Thomas.

This was the next board:

East-West Game
Dealer South

```
                    ♠ 8 6 2
                    ♡ K 9 3
                    ◇ A 9 7 5 2
                    ♣ K 6
    ♠ Q J 5                          ♠ 10 3
    ♡ Q 8                            ♡ J 7 6 4 2
    ◇ Q J 8 3            N           ◇ 10 4
    ♣ J 9 7 3        W     E         ♣ A Q 10 2
                        S
                    ♠ A K 9 7 4
                    ♡ A 10 5
                    ◇ K 6
                    ♣ 8 5 4
```

West	North	East	South
Sister	**Sister**	**Sister**	**Sister**
Katherine	**Carol**	**Theresa**	**Colleen**
-	-	-	1♠
pass	2◇	pass	2♠
pass	3♠	pass	4♠
all pass			

Sister Katherine surveyed her hand nervously. There wasn't much point leading a doubleton heart when she held a natural trump trick anyway. Surely a club was the best idea.

Sister Theresa won the club lead with the queen and switched to a trump, won by declarer's ace. After a club to the king and ace, Sister Colleen won the trump return in her hand and turned her attention to the diamond suit. The two top diamonds and a diamond ruff were followed by a club ruff and another diamond ruff. Finally Sister Colleen crossed to the king of hearts and threw her heart loser on the thirteenth diamond. West was welcome to ruff with her master trump; the defenders scored just two clubs and a trump.

'I shouldn't make that one,' declared Sister Colleen.

Sister Katherine retreated further into her chair, expecting to be blamed for the hand.

Sister Colleen turned to her right, however. 'When you win the second club, you should force dummy with a third round of clubs,' she continued. 'That kills one of the entries I needed to set up the diamonds.'

'You shouldn't criticise other players,' retorted Sister Theresa. 'Weren't you listening to the MD the other day? Self criticism is encouraged but you shouldn't speak any word against your partner or the opponents.'

Sister Colleen smiled in superior fashion. 'You'll make the same mistake next time, if no-one points it out,' she said.

'You Irish never did have any manners,' replied Sister Theresa.

'Can I believe what I'm hearing, girls?' cried Sister Thomas, suddenly appearing at the table. 'Just three minutes after I spoke to you!'

'I was just commending Sister Theresa on her excellent defence,' claimed Sister Colleen.

'Don't make things worse by lying to me,' said Sister Thomas. 'You and Sister Theresa will report to the Mother of Discipline and give her a full account of what you said to each other.'

The two novices exchanged a glance. Rivals they might be, but such an encounter would require some preparation.

'Our noble founder, St Hilda, must be rolling in her grave to witness such poor behaviour,' continued Sister Thomas. 'Do you hear me girls? Rolling in her grave!'

III

The New Novice

osemary Francesca Finucane, an attractive, dark-haired girl from the North of England, stood nervously to attention. In front of her, behind a large desk, were the Mother Superior and the ancient Mother of Discipline.

The Mother Superior smiled warmly. 'There's no need to be frightened, my child,' she said. 'This day is one of the most important in your young life. You are taking the first step on the road towards becoming a nun, the most wonderful calling the world offers. The Sisters here will make you most welcome and, if all goes well, you will become a full member of the order in three years time.'

The Mother of Discipline, who had been four foot ten inches tall in her prime and was now an inch or two shorter than that, surveyed the young girl disapprovingly. Why, she must be nearly six foot tall! If only she herself had been granted a few more inches, her life might have been quite different. She had spent her early years in Colchester and despite being quite pretty (or so her Mother had told her) the local boys had shown no interest in anyone so short. The Good Lord had his reasons for everything, of course, but could he not have shared out the inches more evenly?

'What name shall we choose for you?' said the Mother Superior. She consulted a leather bound book on her desk. 'The names currently available from dearly departed Sisters are... let me see... Bernadette, Imelda Marie, Consumpta and Kathleen.'

The novice's eyes lit up. 'Saint Imelda Marie is an inspiration of mine, Reverend Mother,' she said. 'I would be so proud to bear her name.'

The Mother of Discipline gave a small sigh. 'Have you not heard that Pride is a sin, child?' she demanded. 'The Sisters' names are not chosen according to how beautiful they sound!'

'No indeed, Reverend Mother,' the novice replied. 'I will be happy to accept whatever name is given to me.'

'Give me that book,' said the Mother of Discipline, wincing as she took its full weight. She flipped back several pages. 'I see here, Reverend Mother, that we had a Sister Eustace in the period between 1873 and 1898. That name must surely be available now.'

The Mother Superior nodded. 'We have no Sister of that name, it's true,' she said. 'Would you like that name, my child?'

The young novice swallowed hard. Was she allowed to express an opinion on the matter? Bernadette and Kathleen were such heavenly names, by comparison. Even Sister Consumpta had some sort of ring to it.

'What's the problem, child?' cried the Mother of Discipline. 'Is the name of a Saint who was stoned to death for his Faith not good enough for you?'

'Such a name would be a true blessing, Reverend Mother,' the novice replied. 'I paused only because I did not think I was worthy of the name.'

The Mother Superior repeated her earlier welcoming smile. 'You may feel that way at the moment,' she said. 'In years to come, you will make yourself fully worthy of the name. I am sure of it.'

The Mother Superior retrieved the leather bound book and inscribed the novice's appointed name in it. 'Now, on to other matters,' she said. 'How is your bridge, my child?'

'At the convent school I was rated B-minus for my bidding and B for my cardplay, Reverend Mother.'

The Mother of Discipline exhaled loudly. It was a sign of modern times that they were having to accept such second-rate material nowadays. B-minus for bidding, indeed! Had the girl not listened to her teachers? 'I am in charge of the novices' instruction here,' she declared. 'You will not find me tolerant of those who score marks such as B-minus in the weekly tests.'

The novice blinked nervously. In truth she had received rather more C grades for her bidding. B-minus sounded so much better. 'I will study diligently, Reverend Mother,' she replied. 'I am determined to make my time at St Hilda's a success in every way.'

'Well spoken, indeed!' exclaimed the Mother Superior. 'Now, come this way, er... Sister Eustace. We have a long tour ahead of us. I want to introduce you to every one of our Sisters. We'll start over there, in the Convent laundry. Two of our very best players work in the laundry.'

Sister Eustace thought back to the small, hunched figure they had left behind. The hair-raising stories she had heard about her at the convent school must have been true. What a terror she was!

'Even the Mother of Discipline has a warm side to her,' continued the Mother Superior. 'She has your best interests at heart, you can be sure.'

Sister Eustace followed the Mother Superior through the laundry door. The smell of bleach and detergent was in the air and two nuns could be seen ironing at the far side of the room.

'Yes indeed, Reverend Mother,' she said.

IV

Brian Jesty's Easy Draw

By any standards Brian Jesty's team were moderate performers at the game. They won a round or two of the Gold Cup most years but so much depended on the draw. Last year they had paid their twenty pounds a head, then faced a strong London team in the first round. A concession with eight boards to play was the best they could manage. They were hoping for somewhat better value for money as they awaited their opponents for the first round of the current year's event.

'Any idea who we're playing?' asked Andrew Chatfield, arriving at Jesty's house some time before the match.

'Someone called A. Percival,' Jesty replied. 'I've never heard of him, so we should be in with a chance.'

Some twenty minutes later a small Reinault drew up outside the house. Jesty's team peered anxiously through the net curtains. 'Do you see what I see?' Jesty exclaimed. 'Is this some sort of joke? It's four nuns!'

'Jeez, what a fantastically lucky draw!' Chatfield exclaimed. 'They won't believe this back at the club.'

Jesty laughed. 'Our opponents won't appreciate language like that,' he said. 'You'll have to restrain yourself.'

Brian Jesty opened his front door and looked uncertainly at the four nuns before him. 'Is one of you A. Percival?' he enquired.

The Mother Superior stepped over the threshhold, brushing past him. 'Audrey Percival,' she replied. 'We'll have to warm ourselves by your fire, if you don't mind. The heater in my car has stopped working.'

The match was soon under way and Sister Grace reached a slam on the very first board.

East-West Game
Dealer South

```
                 ♠ K J 6
                 ♡ K 9 7 2
                 ◇ A 8 5 3
                 ♣ 6 4
♠ 10 8 4 3 2                        ♠ A 9 5
♡ Q J 10 6 5        N              ♡ 8 4 3
◇ J              W     E           ◇ Q 10 4
♣ 8 3               S              ♣ J 10 5 2
                 ♠ Q 7
                 ♡ A
                 ◇ K 9 7 6 2
                 ♣ A K Q 9 7
```

West	North	East	South
Brian	**Mother of**	**Andrew**	**Sister**
Jesty	**Discipline**	**Chatfield**	**Grace**
-	-	-	1◇
pass	1♡	pass	3♣
pass	4◇	pass	4♡
pass	6◇	all pass	

Brian Jesty, whose receding hair made him look older than his thirty years, led ♡Q against the diamond slam. Sister Grace won with the ace and paused to consider her prospects. Unless trumps were 2-2 she would have to avoid a loser in spades. How about a low spade from hand at Trick 2? If West held off the ace to 'give declarer a guess', the other spade could be thrown on the heart king.

Sister Grace stole a glance at her left-hand opponent. Was he foolish enough to fall for such a plan? Surely not. Her bidding had suggested short holdings in the major suits. With two low spades and a singleton ace of hearts she would obviously have crossed to the ace of trumps and thrown a spade immediately.

Abandoning this plan, Sister Grace played the king and ace of trumps immediately. When East showed up with a trump trick, the only remaining chance was to throw all of dummy's spades on her club suit. This would be possible only if she could cash four clubs before East ruffed in. 'Small club,' she said.

Chatfield followed with the two in the East seat and Sister Grace took her only chance, finessing the nine. The manoeuvre succeeded and she continued with the three top clubs, throwing two spades from dummy. East had to follow suit and dummy's last spade went away on a fifth round of clubs. The slam had been made.

'Lead a spade, for Heaven's sake!' cried Chatfield. 'I win with the ace and I must score a trump trick. What was the point of leading a heart?'

'I had five of them,' Jesty replied. 'I thought you might be able to ruff.'

Chatfield delivered a withering glance. 'It might just have occurred to me to make a Lightner Double if I was void in hearts,' he said. 'I'll let you explain this one to the others.'

The opponents showed no sign of continuing their discussion, so Sister Grace gave them a gentle nudge. 'I was fortunate in clubs, there, Reverend Mother,' she said. 'If this young gentleman happens to split his club honours, there's no entry back to dummy to play on clubs again.'

Jesty glared at his partner, scribbling a note on his scorecard. 'If I'm going to do the explaining on this one, I'd better get the details right,' he said.

Meanwhile, in Brian Jesty's kitchen, the Mother Superior and Sister Thomas faced Ralph and Pam Cooke, a young married couple who favoured the Precision Club system.

'Have you played in the Gold Cup before?' asked Pam Cooke, giving the Mother Superior a friendly smile.

'Yes, indeed,' the Mother Superior replied. 'Not with much success in recent years, unfortunately.'

'Oh well, never mind,' said Pam Cooke. 'So much depends on who you're drawn against, doesn't it?'

'Quite so,' agreed the Mother Superior. 'We went out to John Collings in the sixth round last year. Couple of slack defences in the last set if I remember rightly.'

Pam looked at her husband in alarm. The sixth round? Perhaps this wasn't such an easy draw after all.

The players drew their cards for this board:

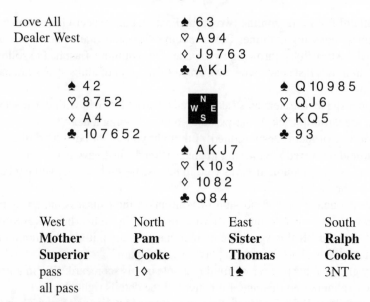

Love All
Dealer West

♠ 6 3
♡ A 9 4
◇ J 9 7 6 3
♣ A K J

♠ 4 2
♡ 8 7 5 2
◇ A 4
♣ 10 7 6 5 2

♠ Q 10 9 8 5
♡ Q J 6
◇ K Q 5
♣ 9 3

♠ A K J 7
♡ K 10 3
◇ 10 8 2
♣ Q 8 4

West	North	East	South
Mother	**Pam**	**Sister**	**Ralph**
Superior	**Cooke**	**Thomas**	**Cooke**
pass	1◇	1♠	3NT
all pass			

The Mother Superior led ♣4 and Cooke won East's queen with the ace. Eight top tricks were on view and it seemed that the diamond suit would have to yield a ninth.

When declarer led ◇2 the Mother Superior rose competently with the ace and played her remaining spade. Cooke won with the jack and played another diamond to East's queen. Sister Thomas proceeded to clear the spade suit, leaving these cards still to be played:

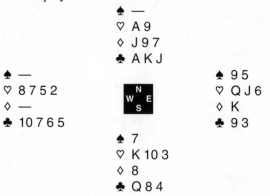

♠ —
♡ A 9
◇ J 9 7
♣ A K J

♠ —
♡ 8 7 5 2
◇ —
♣ 10 7 6 5

♠ 9 5
♡ Q J 6
◇ K
♣ 9 3

♠ 7
♡ K 10 3
◇ 8
♣ Q 8 4

Ralph Cooke surveyed his remaining assets uncertainly. If West held the king of diamonds, he could simply set up the diamond suit. However, East's overcall suggested that she would hold the diamond king. Perhaps something good would happen if he cashed his three club winners.

Sister Thomas followed to two rounds of clubs but had no good discard on the third round. If she threw a spade winner, declarer would be able to knock out her remaining diamond stopper. The only hope was to throw a heart, hoping that her partner held ♡10.

When Sister Thomas threw a heart, Ralph Cooke cashed the ace and king of hearts. The queen and jack fell from East and his ♡10 was good for a ninth trick.

Pam Cooke looked proudly at her husband. 'Well played, Ralph!' she exclaimed. 'That was some sort of squeeze, wasn't it?'

'Yes,' Cooke replied. 'I needed East to hold both heart honours.'

Sister Thomas was tempted to say something but managed to restrain herself.

'They can't possibly play it so well at the other table,' said Pam excitedly. 'It must be a good swing for us.'

This was more than Sister Thomas could stand. 'The contract was cold however the hearts lay,' she declared. 'You should duck the first spade. My partner would be out of spades when she came on lead.'

Ralph Cooke blinked. A hold-up with three stoppers?

'It's the best line, I agree,' observed the Mother Superior. 'A club switch might set up five tricks for the defence but it's not very likely.'

At the other table Sister Grace had just reached game on this deal:

North-South Game
Dealer North

	♠ 9 7 6 5 3 2	
	♡ K 7 3	
	◊ Q 8 5	
	♣ 4	

♠ A J 10 4		♠ 8
♡ —	N	♡ 8 5 4
◊ 9 7 4	W E	◊ K J 10 2
♣ Q J 10 6 5 3	S	♣ A 9 8 7 2

	♠ K Q	
	♡ A Q J 10 9 6 2	
	◊ A 6 3	
	♣ K	

West	North	East	South
Brian	**Mother of**	**Andrew**	**Sister**
Jesty	**Discipline**	**Chatfield**	**Grace**
-	pass	pass	4♡
all pass			

Although there was a small chance that she might miss a slam, Sister Grace had no qualms about opening Four Hearts in the third seat. At unfavourable vulnerability it was quite possible that the opponents had a worthwhile sacrifice somewhere. By opening at the four level she might prevent them from finding it.

Four Hearts was passed out and West led ♣Q to his partner's ace. A spade to the ace and a spade ruff gave the defenders the first three tricks. What now? Chatfield considered his return carefully. Declarer was a strong favourite to hold the diamond ace, so it was far too dangerous to play on that suit. A club return would clearly give a ruff-and-discard, after the fall of South's king, so it would have to be a trump.

Sister Grace covered East's ♡5 with the six. West showed out and she overtook with dummy's seven. She ruffed a spade with the ace and returned to dummy by overtaking the queen of trumps with the king. Another spade ruff with a high trump set up the suit. Sister Grace then overtook her ♡2 with dummy's three and proceeded to cash the two good spades, throwing diamonds from her hand. Ten tricks were there.

'I never wanted that spade ruff,' Chatfield declared. 'I put you on lead so you could play a diamond through.' He wrote the score in his card, inscribing a large star in the margin, his notation for an error by partner. 'Your turn to explain this one to the others,' he said.

'I'm not sure about that,' replied Jesty. 'If you don't ruff the spade, declarer would still lose two diamond tricks. There would be nowhere near enough entries to dummy to set up the spades.'

'Quite so,' said Sister Grace. 'Or you could ruff the spade and give me a ruff-and-discard in clubs. I'm still an entry short.'

When the board was replayed, a quite different auction resulted:

West	North	East	South
Mother	**Pam**	**Sister**	**Ralph**
Superior	**Cooke**	**Thomas**	**Cooke**
-	pass	pass	1♣
3♣	pass	5♣	double
all pass			

Ralph Cooke opened with a strong Precision One Club and the Mother Superior overcalled with a pre-emptive Three Clubs. Pam Cooke felt she should introduce her spades at this stage but such a call would promise at least eight points in the system and Ralph was very strict on such matters. She passed and Sister Thomas raised the ante to Five Clubs.

Ralph Cooke studied his hand unhappily. There was no reason to expect Pam to cover three of his five losers, even though she had hesitated over Three Clubs. And, of course, it would never occur to him take advantage of the hesitation. No, it looked as if he would have to take the money. 'Double,' he said.

There was nothing much to the play. The Mother Superior guessed the trump suit correctly and picked up North's ◊Q. Twelve tricks were there.

'They made it difficult for us,' observed the Mother Superior. 'It's never easy to bid a slam when they open a Precision Club against you.'

Pam gazed admiringly at her husband. The opponents had missed a slam? Good old Ralph! He had certainly fixed them there.

With eight hands still to play, the Convent's lead had grown to some 52 IMPs. By the Mother Superior's reckoning, this was well into concession territory. If the opponents did the decent thing, calling it a day, it might still be possible to return to St Hilda's in time for Vespers.

Brian Jesty poked his head round the door. 'Your choice, I believe,' he said. 'Andrew and I will be in the other room, Ralph and Pam in here.'

The Mother Superior gave a disapproving shake of the head. 'We lead by fifty-two, do you make it?' she queried.

'That's right, fifty-two,' Jesty replied.

Ralph Cooke arrived in a slam on the first board of the final set.

East-West Game	♠ A Q 9 8 7		
Dealer West	♡ 6 2		
	◊ 10 8 7 2		
	♣ 7 3		

♠ —		♠ 5 3
♡ Q 8 3		♡ J 9 7 5 4
◊ Q J 9 3	N W E S	◊ 6
♣ K Q J 5 4 2		♣ A 10 9 8 6

♠ K J 10 6 4 2
♡ A K 10
◊ A K 5 4
♣ —

West	North	East	South
Sister	**Pam**	**Mother of**	**Ralph**
Grace	**Cooke**	**Discipline**	**Cooke**
3♣	pass	5♣	5♠
pass	6♠	all pass	

33

Ralph Cooke ruffed the club lead in his hand and drew trumps. Two rounds of diamonds exposed the bad break in that suit and he sat back in his chair to plan the rest of the play. The only remaining chance seemed to be that East would hold the queen and jack of hearts. Yes, if he could score three heart tricks he would be able to throw one of dummy's diamond losers away.

Declarer crossed to dummy with a trump and played a heart to the 10. Sister Grace won with the queen and proceeded to cash her two diamond winners. The slam was two down.

Pam Cooke looked lovingly at her husband. 'Bad luck, Ralph,' she said. 'You played it beautifully, combining the two chances.'

'Nothing wrong with the contract,' her husband replied. 'Just annoying that the diamonds didn't break. I'd have been OK if East had a singleton diamond honour too.'

'They'll bid it at the other table,' said Pam Cooke. 'There was nothing you could do.'

The Mother of Discipline surveyed her attractive opponent scornfully. Nothing he could do? What rubbish! After cashing one diamond he should have eliminated the hearts and clubs, then played a low diamond towards the 10. She had rarely seen a more trivial endplay.

'It'll be a flat board,' continued Pam Cooke. 'Don't worry about it.'

The Mother of Discipline inscribed the +100 in her scorecard, adding a large 14 in the IMPs column. Flat board, the girl must be joking. The good Lord might have granted her a pretty face but she had very little brain to go with it.

At the other table the Mother Superior had not relaxed her effort in the slightest, despite the huge lead. If the opponents were determined not to concede in such circumstances, it was her custom to extract the maximum number of IMPs from the extra boards played.

```
Game All              ♠ A K 9 2
Dealer West           ♡ K J 8 5
                      ◊ 10 3
                      ♣ A K 8

       ♠ Q J 10 5 3              ♠ 8
       ♡ A                       ♡ 9 4 2
       ◊ K Q 9 6         N       ◊ 8 7 5 4 2
       ♣ J 10 4       W     E    ♣ 9 7 5 3
                         S
                      ♠ 7 6 4
                      ♡ Q 10 7 6 3
                      ◊ A J
                      ♣ Q 6 2
```

West	North	East	South
Brian	**Sister**	**Andrew**	**Mother**
Jesty	**Thomas**	**Chatfield**	**Superior**
1♠	double	pass	3♡
pass	4♡	all pass	

Brian Jesty led ♠Q against Four Hearts and the Mother Superior won with dummy's ace. A trump to the queen was taken by West's ace and Jesty continued with ♠J.

The Mother Superior could see what would happen if she covered with dummy's king. East would ruff and switch to a diamond. Leading a spade towards the nine would then be in vain, since West could step in with the 10 and cash a diamond trick. 'Small, please,' said the Mother Superior.

Jesty's ♠J held the trick and he continued with a low spade. The Mother Superior covered with dummy's nine and the contract was assured. East ruffed and returned a diamond but declarer was able to win with the ace and draw the outstanding trump. It remained only to cross to dummy to discard the losing diamond on the king of spades. Ten tricks had been made.

'Well played, Reverend Mother,' congratulated Sister Thomas.

'It was child's play after the 1♠ opening,' the Mother Superior replied. 'I hope I would have found the same play without it.'

Two good cards from the St Hilda's pairs bumped the winning margin to more than eighty IMPs and the Convent team were at last able to don their overcoats.

'Good luck in the next round,' said Brian Jesty, not sounding as if he meant it.

The Mother Superior stepped out into the street, where a cold wind was blowing. 'It's a real nuisance that my heater has packed up,' she declared. 'It won't be the most pleasant of journeys home.'

'The new novice, Sister Eustace, is quite adept at mechanical matters,' declared Sister Thomas. 'Perhaps you could ask her to look at it.'

'Thanks for the tip,' replied the Mother Superior. 'I'm certainly not letting Sister Bernadine near it again. Not after that time when she shorted the battery.'

'Perhaps the Good Lord intends us all to freeze to death,' quipped Sister Grace, pulling her coat around her as she took one of the back seats.

The Mother of Discipline scowled disapprovingly. 'You wouldn't joke about such things if you had my poor circulation,' she declared. 'Come on, let's get going!'

V

Sister Thomas's Poor Session

With a sigh Sister Thomas ran a finger down her scorecard. Half a top above average at best and there were only three rounds to go. Ah well, if three weak pairs arrived, bearing tops, it might still be possible to finish in a respectable position. Her prayers appeared to have been answered when Sister Benedict and Sister Myrtle arrived at the table.

'Good evening to you,' said Sister Benedict, brushing some imaginary specks of dust off her chair before sitting down. 'Sister Myrtle and I are trying something new tonight. Culpepper cue-bid overcalls.'

The Mother Superior, who was barely able to suppress her amusement at this, feigned concern. 'Did you hear that, partner?' she said. 'We will have to plan a defence to this.'

'They haven't actually come up yet,' continued Sister Benedict, 'but a cue-bid in one major shows six cards in the other major and four cards in an unspecified minor.'

'It's the other way round, isn't it?' queried Sister Myrtle. 'Four cards in the major and six in the minor.'

'Is it?' replied Sister Benedict. 'Just as well you reminded me before I got it wrong.'

'Four-six shape,' said the Mother Superior. 'I think I've heard of that. Isn't that the Culpepper method?'

'You know it!' exclaimed Sister Benedict. 'The scheme was invented by Hugh Culpepper. An aunt of mine actually knows him; he plays in her local church hall.'

'It's a small world,' declared the Mother Superior. 'Shall we start?'

First to speak, the capacious Sister Myrtle sorted through this hand:

♠ K 10 7 2
♡ K Q 8 4
♦ A 7 6 2
♣ 5

Now, what were you meant to open on 4-4-4-1 hands? The suit below the singleton, was it? No, that couldn't be right; there wasn't any suit below the singleton. It must be the suit above the singleton. 'One Diamond,' said Sister Myrtle.

Her partner responded Two Clubs and Sister Myrtle paused to consider her rebid. She couldn't bid Two Hearts or Two Spades because they would be reverse-bids and she wasn't strong enough for that. What about 2NT? No, that was strong too, the way they played it.

Sister Myrtle gave a puzzled shake of the head. It seemed that the hand was unbiddable at Acol. Perhaps she should pass? A distant memory stirred of some hand where she had passed on a similar sequence. Sister Benedict had said something unpleasant and told everyone in the Convent about it. No, she really must find some rebid or other, preferably something weak-sounding. 'Two Diamonds,' said Sister Myrtle.

She soon found herself in 3NT. This was the full deal:

Love All
Dealer South

♠ A Q 4
♡ J 7 3
♦ 9
♣ A 10 7 6 4 2

♠ 9 8 2
♡ A 6 2
♦ K Q 8 4 3
♣ Q 8

♠ J 6 5
♡ 10 9 5
♦ J 10 5
♣ K J 9 3

♠ K 10 7 3
♡ K Q 8 4
♦ A 7 6 2
♣ 5

West	North	East	South
Sister Thomas	**Sister Benedict**	**Mother Superior**	**Sister Myrtle**
-	-	-	1♦
pass	2♣	pass	2♦
pass	3♣	pass	3NT
all pass			

Disinclined to lead a diamond after South had bid and rebid the suit, Sister Thomas placed ♠8 on the table. Sister Myrtle won with the 10 and played a heart to the jack, followed by a heart to the king and ace. Sister Thomas switched to the queen of clubs but Sister Myrtle was able to win in dummy and claim nine tricks when the hearts divided 3-3.

'Appallingly bad dummy play,' exclaimed Sister Thomas

The triumphant smile on Sister Myrtle's face faded. 'I thought I played it rather well,' she said.

'I'm referring to your play in the heart suit,' continued Sister Thomas. 'You should win the spade lead in dummy, then lead twice towards the hearts in your hand. That gains when the Reverend Mother holds a doubleton ace.'

Sister Myrtle was somewhat mystified. 'I thought you had the ace,' she replied.

Sister Thomas looked despairingly at the ceiling. Why did people with so little feeling for the game *play* bridge?

Sister Benedict peered through her horn-rimmed spectacles at the travelling scoresheet. 'You can't have played it that badly, partner,' she said. 'It's a top! No-one else managed to make it.'

'They must have played on clubs instead of hearts,' replied Sister Myrtle. 'Easy mistake to make.'

The Mother Superior leaned forward. 'Unfortunate lead, partner,' she said. 'A diamond lead beats it easily.'

Sister Thomas reached for Sister Myrtle's curtain card, gazing at the diamond holding in disbelief. 'It's just possible that the bidding was different at the other tables,' she said.

The penultimate round brought strong opponents to Sister Thomas's table, the Mother of Discipline and Sister Grace.

'Good evening,' said Sister Grace, smiling in friendly fashion as she took her seat. 'Are you two doing well, as usual?'

Sister Thomas failed to return the smile. 'Since you ask, we've had one or two unlucky ones,' she replied.

The Mother Superior winked at Sister Grace. 'Sister Myrtle was in fine form against us,' she said. 'She outplayed the field to score a top in 3NT.'

An unamused Sister Thomas motioned for the play to start. This was the first board of the round:

Love All
Dealer South

	♠ K J 10 7 2	
	♡ A Q 6	
	◊ K 4	
	♣ K 8 3	

♠ Q 6 5 3		♠ 9 8 4
♡ 9 7 4 2	N W E S	♡ K J 10 8 3
◊ Q 10 3		◊ 7
♣ Q 6		♣ 10 9 5 2

	♠ A	
	♡ 5	
	◊ A J 9 8 6 5 2	
	♣ A J 7 4	

West	North	East	South
Sister	**Mother of**	**Mother**	**Sister**
Thomas	**Discipline**	**Superior**	**Grace**
-	-	-	1◊
pass	1♠	pass	2◊
pass	3NT	pass	4♣
pass	4◊	pass	4♡
pass	4NT	pass	5♣
pass	6◊	all pass	

The Mother of Discipline's 4NT was Roman Key-card Blackwood, the response showing either three aces or two aces and the king of trumps. Sister Thomas led ♡7 against Six Diamonds and Sister Grace called for dummy's ace, East signalling heavily with the jack. Entries to dummy were scarce, so declarer cashed the ace of spades, then played the ace and king of trumps, East showing out on the second round.

The king of spades was followed by the jack, East producing the nine. Sister Grace had no intention of running the spade, since several other chances were still alive. She ruffed in the South hand, West following with a low card.

When Sister Thomas was thrown in with a trump she returned another round of hearts. Sister Grace was fairly sure from East's signal at trick one that the king of hearts was offside. She played low from dummy, preserving the queen as a threat card. Ruffing the trick in the South hand, she proceeded to run the trump suit. This was the resultant end position:

M. of Discipline
- ♠ 10
- ♡ Q
- ◇ —
- ♣ K 8

Sr. Thomas
- ♠ Q
- ♡ 9
- ◇ —
- ♣ Q 6

```
  N
W   E
  S
```

M. Superior
- ♠ —
- ♡ K
- ◇ —
- ♣ 10 9 5

Sr. Grace
- ♠ —
- ♡ —
- ◇ 5
- ♣ A J 7

The last trump drew a heart from West and a spade from dummy. The Mother Superior had to retain her guard on dummy's queen of hearts and therefore threw a club. Sister Grace now played king and another club, the nine and 10 appearing from East. Since East's last card was assumed to be the king of hearts, a club finesse could not succeed. Sister Grace rose with the ace and claimed the slam when West's queen came down.

'Not too difficult,' observed Sister Grace. 'I expect several other declarers will take the same line.'

Fat chance, thought Sister Thomas. She stole a brief glance to her left as the scoresheet was unrolled. Yes, only two other pairs had bid the slam and neither had made it.

'Would you like to see the scoresheet?' croaked the Mother of Discipline.

Sister Thomas shook her head. 'No need to,' she replied. 'Present company excepted, no-one in this establishment is capable of bidding and making a simple slam.'

This was the next board:

East-West Game
Dealer East

```
               ♠ A K 8 5
               ♡ J 9 7 5 4
               ◇ A K 5
               ♣ 6
♠ 9 4                          ♠ Q 10 3 2
♡ 6 3              N           ♡ K Q
◇ J 9 6 3 2    W     E         ◇ Q 10 7
♣ 10 9 8 2         S           ♣ K Q J 3
               ♠ J 7 6
               ♡ A 10 8 2
               ◇ 8 4
               ♣ A 7 5 4
```

West	North	East	South
Sister	**Mother of**	**Mother**	**Sister**
Thomas	**Discipline**	**Superior**	**Grace**
-	-	1♣	pass
pass	double	pass	2♡
pass	4NT	pass	5♡
pass	6♡	all pass	

Sister Thomas gave a weary sigh as, once again, the cards lay with the opponents. She led ♣10, not thinking much of the defenders' prospects when declarer won with the ace.

Prospects were less promising from Sister Grace's viewpoint. It seemed she might need the spade queen to fall doubleton, unless... well, if East held only four clubs an elimination might be possible.

Sister Grace ruffed a club at Trick 2. She returned to her hand with the ace of trumps, East's queen falling, and ruffed another club. The club nine had not yet appeared from West's hand, so the prospects of a 4-4 club break had brightened. Two rounds of diamonds and a diamond ruff eliminated that suit and declarer now ruffed her last club.

This position had been reached:

M. of Discipline
♠ A K 8 5
♡ J
♢ —
♣ —

Sr. Thomas
♠ 9 4
♡ 6
♢ J 9
♣ —

```
  N
W   E
  S
```

M. Superior
♠ Q 10 3 2
♡ K
♢ —
♣ —

Sr. Grace
♠ J 7 6
♡ 10 8
♢ —
♣ —

'Trump, please,' said Sister Grace.

The Mother Superior won with the king of trumps and now had to play a spade. Sister Grace rose with the jack and, with a small chuckle, claimed the slam. 'That was a lucky one,' she said.

'Not the best of leads, Sister,' observed the Mother Superior. 'Lead a trump and you take out one of declarer's entries prematurely. She can't ruff all her clubs then. I'd have a safe exit when she threw me in.'

Pardon me for living, thought Sister Thomas. Since when had a trump been a good lead against a small slam? Any lead but a club would have been the wildest of gambles.

The last round of the evening brought two of the stronger novices to Sister Thomas's table. She inspected the youngsters' convention card closely, not wanting to be caught out by some esoteric opening. 'You're playing a strong notrump?' she exclaimed.

'We're trying it out for a session or two, Sister,' replied Sister Colleen. 'A lot of the top players use a strong notrump nowadays.'

Sister Thomas raised a bushy eyebrow. 'Oh, so you're top players now, are you?'

'No, indeed, Sister,' said Sister Colleen, 'but it's always interesting to try something new.'

North-South Game
Dealer North

```
                    ♠ A 10 7 3
                    ♡ K J 4 2
                    ♦ J 3
                    ♣ A J 5
   ♠ Q                              ♠ K 9 8 4 2
   ♡ 6                              ♡ 10 7 5
   ♦ A 9 7 5          N             ♦ K 10 8 6
   ♣ K Q 8 7 6 4 3  W   E           ♣ 9
                      S
                    ♠ J 6 5
                    ♡ A Q 9 8 3
                    ♦ Q 4 2
                    ♣ 10 2
```

West	North	East	South
Sister	**Sister**	**Mother**	**Sister**
Thomas	**Carol**	**Superior**	**Colleen**
-	1♣	1♠	2♡
3♣	3♡	pass	4♡
all pass			

Sister Carol opened 1♣, the system bid on all weak notrump hands. With an eye on the vulnerability, the Mother Superior ventured a 1♠ overcall. Sister Colleen responded 2♡ and Sister Thomas spent a while considering what action to take. With the other players all bidding, it was surprising that she should hold 11 points. She could hardly pass with such values but the 'short club' had made life very awkward. 'Three Clubs,' she said eventually.

The Mother Superior alerted the bid. 'Yes?' said Sister Carol.

'The cue bid shows a sound raise to the three level in spades,' replied the Mother Superior.

North supported her partner's hearts and Sister Colleen then thumbed through her cards uncertainly. There was little justification for bidding on. Still, after East's overcall and the sound raise, was it not obvious that partner would be very short in spades? If partner had a singleton spade and fair values in the minors it might be possible to make ten tricks. 'Four Hearts,' said Sister Colleen.

The spade queen was led and down went the dummy. The young declarer could not believe it when she saw four spades there. Four Hearts looked hopeless. Mind you, she could hardly call the Director and complain that the Mother Superior had given her a bad explanation of the 3♣ bid. Sister Colleen smiled to herself. What a thought! 'Ace, please,' she said.

The ace and king of trumps revealed the 3-1 break and Sister Colleen then led a spade towards her hand. The Mother Superior could not afford to put up the spade king or declarer would have three spade tricks and a discard for her club loser. She played low and South's ♠J won the trick.

Sister Colleen drew a third round of trumps and led a low diamond towards dummy. Sister Thomas played low and the Mother Superior won the jack with her king. Since she could still not afford to cash the spade king, she returned a diamond to the queen and West's ace. Sister Thomas switched to the king of clubs but the contract could no longer be beaten. Declarer won with the ace and cleared a second club trick for herself. Her last spade went away on the jack of clubs and the game had been made.

The Mother Superior smiled sympathetically across the table. 'Unlucky choice of leads again, partner,' she said. 'Lead the king of clubs and it must go down.'

'That's right,' said Sister Colleen. 'You can cash the club queen when you get in, Sister. One discard is no use to me.'

For a moment Sister Thomas had to check that this was not some bad dream. It was surely automatic to lead a singleton in the suit that partner had overcalled. And since when was an 18-year-old novice entitled to speak in such a cavalier fashion to one of the Convent's most senior nuns?

Sister Carol inserted the top on the scoresheet and beamed at her partner. 'The strong notrump is really good, isn't it?' she said. 'We'd never have got there if I'd opened a weak notrump. You only had nine points.'

Sister Thomas's mouth fell open. It went against all of St Hilda's teachings to display pleasure in such an open manner. Was the Mother Superior going to say nothing at all?

The Mother Superior smiled indulgently at the two young novices. How heart-warming it was to see them enjoying the game so much. 'You shouldn't really gloat at a good result, girls,' she said. 'Particularly as you only made it because of a poor opening lead.'

VI

Father O'Regan's Visit

Every Tuesday Father O'Regan visited the Convent to hear the nuns' confessions. The senior nuns would confess after Primes. The novices had to wait until late afternoon, before Vespers.

'Bless me, Father, for I have sinned,' said the blonde-haired novice, Sister Carol. 'This is my first confession for seven days.'

'What are your sins, my child?' enquired Father O'Regan, fingering his beard. According to the older nuns his beard had once been a glorious red in colour. Now it was a sad wispy mixture of grey, brown and white.

'I was jealous of Sister Ambrosine and Sister Perpetua when they finished third in the main pairs last Thursday,' said Sister Carol.

'The successes of your colleagues should be a source of joy to you,' declared the priest. 'You will say three Our Father's and offer a prayer that Sister Ambrosine and Sister Perpetua do well next Thursday, too. What else do you wish to confess?'

'Something so bad I can hardly bring myself to mention it, Father,' replied Sister Carol.

'It must not sit on your conscience, my child,' Father O'Regan declared. 'Show true contrition for your sin and it will be forgiven.'

'In last week's pairs I found myself looking at the MD's hand,' continued Sister Carol.

'MD?' queried the priest.

'The Mother of Discipline, Father,' said Sister Carol. 'She holds her cards so low. I didn't really mean to look but my eyes just happened to wander in that direction. I saw that she had only one trump and king-jack to four diamonds.'

'It sounds more like an accident, my child,' said Father O'Regan. 'As long as you took no advantage of it, no harm was done.'

'But I did take advantage of it,' continued Sister Carol. 'I took the right view in trumps, finessing her partner for the queen, then I played for a partial elimination. I was the only declarer to make the contract.'

Sister Carol feared the worst as there was a long pause from behind the grille. Perhaps she shouldn't have mentioned it. Or she could have left out the bit about playing the hand differently.

'To take advantage of the old and afflicted is a sad thing, my child,' declared the priest, who had adopted a more severe tone of voice. 'You will say ten Glory Be's and apologise humbly to the Mother of Discipline, explaining exactly what you did. Is it too late to have the score corrected?'

Sister Carol suddenly felt rather ill. Apologise to the MD directly? Why on earth had she mentioned the matter? No-one would ever have known. 'I think it's too late to correct the scores, Father,' she replied. 'Sister Bernardine has already issued the masterpoint certificates.'

'Very well,' said Father O'Regan. 'Do not let me heard of any similar behaviour again. I will not be so lenient next time.'

Sister Carol staggered out of the confessional. Lenient? At the moment she would rather die than have to tell the Mother of Discipline that she had been peeking at her cards.

The Irish novice, Sister Colleen, was next to step into the confessional. 'Bless me, Father, for I have sinned,' she said. 'It is one week since my last confession.'

'What sins have you committed, my child?' asked Father O'Regan.

'I felt superior to Sister Eustace when she went off in a heart slam she should have made,' said Sister Colleen. 'My mother sent me a box of chocolate mints and I failed to share them with my fellow Sisters. And I overslept last Friday and was five minutes late for Lauds.'

'Do you not have an alarm clock, Sister?' reprimanded Father O'Regan. 'What about Sister Eustace's heart slam? Was there any interest in it?'

Sister Colleen extracted an old scorecard from her habit and scribbled this hand on the back:

♠ K x x
♥ Q 9 x x
♦ A 9 x x
♣ A x

♠ A J x
♥ A K J 10 x
♦ K Q 8 x
♣ x

'It was something like this, Father,' she said, passing the scorecard under the grille that separated them. 'She opened One Heart and West overcalled Two Clubs. North bid Three Clubs, to show a sound raise and East bid Five Clubs. Sister Eustace bid Six Hearts and the king of clubs was led.'

'Yes, I see,' replied Father O'Regan. 'Well, I win and draw trumps. How do they break?'

'West has three trumps, Father.'

'Now it must be right to play the king of diamonds,' continued Father O'Regan. 'If an honour falls on either side, you can play for it to be a singleton by cashing the appropriate diamond honour next.'

'No diamond honour falls, Father.'

'Well, I'm still OK if West has the four diamonds,' declared Father O'Regan. 'I can ruff the last club and exit to West on the fourth round of diamonds. She will have to give a ruff-and-discard or lead into the spade tenace.'

'It's a clever line of play, Father,' said Sister Colleen.

Father O'Regan nodded happily to himself. Mind you, it was not surprising that young Sister Eustace had missed such a line. As for feeling superior when declarer went down, there was little excuse for that. Still, the girl was only young. Two Hail Mary's would be ample in the circumstances.

'In fact it was East who held four diamonds,' continued Sister Colleen.

Father O'Regan, who was beginning to lose interest in the hand, pushed the scorecard back under the grille.

'Instead of exiting in diamonds, you should play ace, king and another spade,' said Sister Colleen. 'The defender who wins the trick will be endplayed, however the diamonds lie.'

'Yes, I see that now,' replied Father O'Regan gruffly. 'I could barely read your writing. I would have made it at the table, of course.'

'Yes indeed, Father.'

'Say five Hail Mary's and five Glory Be's,' said Father O'Regan. 'And remember me next time you receive a parcel from your mother. Chocolate mints are a favourite of mine.'

Occasionally Father O'Regan would remain at the Convent following the confessions. After partaking of the usual frugal supper, he would compete in the Tuesday duplicate. Today was one such occasion and he found himself partnering the Mother of Discipline.

An early round produced the first slam hand.

North-South Game
Dealer South

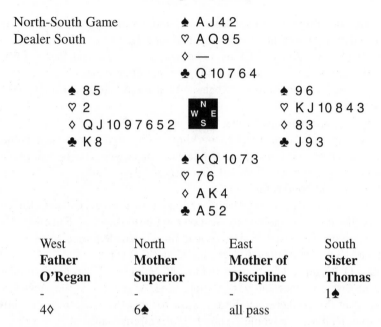

♠ A J 4 2
♡ A Q 9 5
◊ —
♣ Q 10 7 6 4

♠ 8 5
♡ 2
◊ Q J 10 9 7 6 5 2
♣ K 8

♠ 9 6
♡ K J 10 8 4 3
◊ 8 3
♣ J 9 3

♠ K Q 10 7 3
♡ 7 6
◊ A K 4
♣ A 5 2

West	North	East	South
Father	**Mother**	**Mother of**	**Sister**
O'Regan	**Superior**	**Discipline**	**Thomas**
-	-	-	1♠
4◊	6♠	all pass	

Father O'Regan led ♡2 and down went the dummy. Sister Thomas viewed its contents impassively. Despite an overload of top cards in her own hand, the slam was by no means certain to make. The duplication in diamonds was the problem. Her seven points in that suit were virtually useless. What could be done?

There was no chance whatsoever of the heart finesse succeeding, concluded Sister Thomas. West's ♡2 had the air of a singleton, in fact. If that were the case, it might be possible to make the slam by setting up the clubs. Yes, if West held the king of clubs she should be able to set up the clubs without allowing East to gain the lead.

Sister Thomas won the first trick with the ace of hearts and drew trumps in two rounds with the king and ace. When she played a club to the ace, Father O'Regan paused for thought before playing to the trick. If he played low, it was clear that the defenders would score the king of clubs but no further trick. Perhaps he should unblock the king under the ace? His partner surely held the jack of clubs or declarer would have taken a finesse in the suit. Yes! Unblock the king of clubs and partner might then get in with the jack to cash her heart trick.

When the king of clubs appeared under her ace, Sister Thomas drew in air between her ill-formed teeth. What now? Should she play a club to the queen and a third club? This would drop East's doubleton jack of clubs if West had made a clever unblock from three clubs to the king. It would succeed also, of course, if West held K-J-x in the club suit.

Sister Thomas soon spotted something better. She cashed two top diamonds, throwing hearts from the dummy. She then ruffed her last diamond, arriving at this end position:

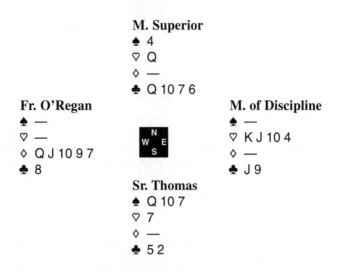

M. Superior
♠ 4
♡ Q
♢ —
♣ Q 10 7 6

Fr. O'Regan
♠ —
♡ —
♢ Q J 10 9 7
♣ 8

M. of Discipline
♠ —
♡ K J 10 4
♢ —
♣ J 9

Sr. Thomas
♠ Q 10 7
♡ 7
♢ —
♣ 5 2

When the queen of hearts was led from the table, the Mother of Discipline was endplayed. With somewhat ill grace she tossed her remaining cards face-up on the table, conceding the slam.

The Mother Superior smiled warmly at Father O'Regan. 'A brilliant defence, throwing the club king,' she exclaimed. 'It deserved to succeed.'

Father O'Regan was delighted at the compliment. 'Sometimes virtue must be its own reward, Reverend Mother,' he replied. 'Sister Thomas is also deserving of our praise. It was a fine endplay.'

The Mother of Discipline did not appear to share this opinion. She glared at the bushy-eyed declarer, who was already sorting out her cards for the next board. Would it have been too much to allow the Father to beat the slam? After everything he had done for the Sisters over the past thirty years?

The last round of the evening brought Sister Colleen and her partner to Father O'Regan's table. The priest reached a slam on this deal:

Game All   ♠ J 8
Dealer North   ♡ 7 2
                    ◊ A J 10 7
                    ♣ A K Q 7 5

♠ K Q 9 6 5		♠ 10 7 2
♡ 4	N W E S	♡ Q 8 6 3
◊ Q 8 4 2		◊ K 5
♣ 10 8 6		♣ J 9 4 2

                    ♠ A 4 3
                    ♡ A K J 10 9 5
                    ◊ 9 6 3
                    ♣ 3

West	North	East	South
Sister	**Mother of**	**Sister**	**Father**
Colleen	**Discipline**	**Carol**	**O'Regan**
-	1♣	pass	2♡
pass	3◊	pass	4♡
pass	6♡	all pass	

Sister Colleen led the king of spades against the heart slam, looking slightly surprised at the dummy that was displayed. No spade control? If she or Sister Carol had potted a slam like that, the MD would have been reaching for her punishment book.

Father O'Regan won the spade lead with the ace and played three rounds of clubs, throwing his remaining spades. A successful finesse of the jack of trumps was followed by a diamond to the jack and king. When Sister Carol played back the jack of clubs, declarer ruffed with the 10. It seemed to Sister Colleen that declarer was missing the queen of trumps. On the fourth round of clubs she tried the effect of discarding the queen of diamonds.

Father O'Regan viewed this card with interest. If he tried to cross to dummy in diamonds for another trump finesse, West would surely ruff. Yes, he would have to play trumps from the top, hoping for a 3-2 break.

When the ace of trumps was played Sister Colleen showed out, discarding a spade. Muttering something unsuitable for novices' ears, the priest attempted a belated trump reduction. He crossed to the diamond ace, annoyed to see West follow suit, and ruffed dummy's last spade. His last three cards were ♡K9 ◊9. If a diamond to dummy stood up, he would be able to claim the last two tricks on a trump coup. Please the Lord that the diamonds would be 3-3.

The prayer failed to reach its destination. East ruffed the third round of diamonds and the slam was one down.

'What happened there in diamonds?' demanded the Mother of Discipline. She turned towards Sister Colleen. 'What was your diamond holding?'

Sister Colleen was trying hard not to look pleased with herself. 'Queen doubleton, Reverend Mother,' she replied. 'And another two small ones.'

'I suppose you think that's clever, tricking poor old Father O'Regan like that,' persisted the Mother of Discipline. 'He cycles nearly ten miles each way, every single Tuesday, just to hear our confessions. And how do you reward him? You trick him!'

'I'm very sorry, Reverend Mother,' said Sister Colleen. 'I thought it was part of the game.'

Father O'Regan did not like to look foolish, particularly in front of two novices. He caught the Mother of Discipline's eye. 'Did the young Sister here come to see you after confession this afternoon?' he enquired.

'She did, yes,' replied the Mother of Discipline. 'I was very sorry to hear of her lapse. She will recite three Confiteor's to remind her not to err in the same way again.'

'You were in a lenient mood!' declared the priest. 'Three Confiteor's for peeking at your hand during last week's game. I'd have thought bare-faced cheating such as that was a far more severe matter.'

The Mother of Discipline's eyes bulged almost to the point of bursting. 'Peeking at my hand!' she cried. 'You wicked girl. You told me some garbled story about playing against the odds, taking a backward finesse.'

'I'm sure a suitable punishment will come to mind,' declared Father O'Regan. 'In the mean time, perhaps you can enter an adjusted result on the scoresheet. Deception of any sort is not allowed within the Convent. Never has been and never will!'

VII

Emily Blunkett's Missed Opportunity

The Mother Superior had a clear idea of the mission of St Hilda's in the local community. It was not her intention that the Sisters should withdraw behind the Convent walls, spending their days hoeing the vegetable beds and praying for the world's poor. No, they must mix with the local inhabitants and spread their ideas about life to a wider audience.

With this aim in mind, she had entered a team in the district bridge league the previous year. The first season had proved somewhat embarrassing. As a new team they had been placed in the second division, where the level of play was modest in the extreme. After blitzing all the teams there by at least 60 IMPs over 24 boards, they had been promoted to the first division.

'I wonder if the standard will be any better in the top division,' said the Mother of Discipline, beckoning for Sister Thomas to help her on with overcoat. 'I never play at my best when the opponents are hopeless.'

'Time will tell,' replied the Mother Superior. 'There's no need for us to field our top team every time, if the standard does prove to be weak.'

The first match of the new season was against a team captained by Bill Blunkett. A retired landscape gardener, he lived with his wife in a small thatched cottage a mile from the Convent.

'What a beautiful evening!' exclaimed Sister Grace. 'Why don't we walk to the match?'

The Mother of Discipline could not believe what she was hearing. Walk? If Sister Grace suffered from a right hip like her own, she would not have made such an inconsiderate suggestion.

The Mother Superior reached for her car keys. 'There's no time to walk,' she declared. 'We'll barely be there by seven o'clock as it is.'

The first half of the match placed the Mother of Discipline against Bill and Emily Blunkett. This was an early board:

```
Game All              ♠ J 8 5
Dealer North          ♡ K 4
                      ◇ K J 9
                      ♣ A 10 9 7 4
   ♠ —                              ♠ K 10 9 7
   ♡ Q J 9 7 6 5        N           ♡ 10 2
   ◇ Q 8 6 5         W     E        ◇ 10 3 2
   ♣ Q 6 2             S            ♣ K J 5 3
                      ♠ A Q 6 4 3 2
                      ♡ A 8 3
                      ◇ A 7 4
                      ♣ 8
```

West	North	East	South
Bill Blunkett	**Mother of Discipline**	**Emily Blunkett**	**Sister Grace**
-	1♣	pass	1♠
pass	2♣	pass	6♠
all pass			

It was Sister Grace's policy to give away as little information as possible during the auction. Conscious that she was making a slight overbid, she leapt to Six Spades on the second round of bidding.

'That's unusual,' said Bill Blunkett. 'We always use Blackwood before bidding a slam.'

'Or Gerber,' added his wife. 'I prefer that, really. It keeps you at a safer level.'

Sister Grace smiled politely. 'You may be right,' she replied. 'I decided not to on this occasion.'

Bill Blunkett led the queen of hearts and down went the dummy. 'Very nice, Reverend Mother,' observed Sister Grace. Yes, she could ruff one heart, give up a trump trick if necessary, then play to set up a long club to dispose of the diamond loser. 'King of hearts, please.'

A finesse of the trump queen succeeded but West showed out, throwing a heart. Sister Grace paused to re-assess the position, which was nowhere near as bright as it had been a few seconds ago. To escape for one trump loser, she would have to endplay East to lead away from the trump king at Trick 12. This would not be possible after taking a heart ruff in dummy; dummy's jack would then be bare and could be pinned by a king of trumps exit. No, she would need the diamond finesse to work and East's shape to be exactly right.

Sister Grace crossed to the ace of clubs and ruffed a club. She then played a diamond to the jack, pleased to see this card win. A second club ruff was followed by the ace and king of diamonds and a third club ruff. Sister Grace cashed the ace of hearts to leave this end position:

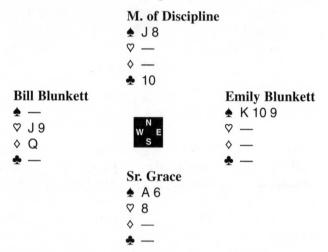

M. of Discipline
♠ J 8
♡ —
♢ —
♣ 10

Bill Blunkett
♠ —
♡ J 9
♢ Q
♣ —

Emily Blunkett
♠ K 10 9
♡ —
♢ —
♣ —

Sr. Grace
♠ A 6
♡ 8
♢ —
♣ —

Declarer's ♡8 was covered by West's nine. Sister Grace discarded the club from dummy and a distressed East found that she had to ruff partner's winner. Worse than that, she then had to lead away from the trump king. Sister Grace ran the ♠10 exit to dummy's jack and twelve tricks were there.

'You made it?' queried Emily Blunkett. 'I can hardly believe that.'

'It was very lucky,' replied Sister Grace.

'There's no way that Judith and Ronnie will make that one,' continued Emily Blunkett. 'Once declarer played a trump to the queen, I had two certain trump tricks!'

'I don't expect they'll bid it, either,' her husband declared. 'There were only 26 points between the two hands. That should be a game contract according to Ron Klinger's flipper.'

At the other table Ronald Gross was sitting South. His well-cut Saville Row business suit bore witness to the success of the accountancy firm bearing his name. He had just picked up these cards:

♠ K Q J 4
♡ 8 6 5
◊ Q 10 3
♣ A 9 5

'One Heart,' said his impeccably coiffed wife, Judith.

Gross responded 1♠ and the Mother Superior intervened with 2◊.

'Four Spades,' said Judith.

Ronald Gross surveyed his hand at length. Should he make a slam try? Good trumps, yes, and a useful ace of clubs... but no control in the diamond suit. Best to be cautious in this world. 'No bid,' he said eventually.

The Mother Superior led the king of diamonds and this proved to be the full deal:

East-West Game
Dealer North

```
                      ♠ A 8 5 3
                      ♡ A K Q 7 2
                      ◊ 5
                      ♣ Q 10 4
   ♠ 10 9 6 2                          ♠ 7
   ♡ 3                N                ♡ J 10 9 4
   ◊ A K J 9 7 6 4  W   E              ◊ 8 2
   ♣ 2                S                ♣ K J 8 7 6 3
                      ♠ K Q J 4
                      ♡ 8 6 5
                      ◊ Q 10 3
                      ♣ A 9 5
```

West	North	East	South
Mother	**Judith**	**Sister**	**Ronald**
Superior	**Gross**	**Thomas**	**Gross**
-	1♡	pass	1♠
2◊	4♠	all pass	

Judith Gross looked somewhat worried as she laid out the dummy. 'You were thinking of a slam, Ronnie, I realise,' she said. 'I hope this is not too good.'

Ronald Gross surveyed the dummy. Too good, she says. Since when was a miserable fifteen points enough for a jump to the four-level? Still, how many tricks did he have? If the breaks were good, five heart tricks, four trump tricks and the ace of clubs. That was ten and two diamond ruffs would bring the total to twelve! Judith would say he had not trusted her bidding – he could picture the scene now.

'You are a bit good,' Ronald Gross replied. 'Maybe a splinter bid of Four Diamonds would be better.'

The lead of a king had requested a length signal and Sister Grace duly played the eight to the first trick. The Mother Superior switched to her singleton club and this drew East's jack and declarer's ace.

Now, thought Gross, how should the play go? Diamond ruff, trump to the jack, diamond ruff with the ace, trump to the king and draw the last trump with the queen. That is how he would have played Six Spades. Maybe he should look for a safer line in Four Spades.

Gross drew two rounds of trumps with the king and queen, not displeased to see East show out on the second round. At least Judith would not be able to blame him for missing a slam now. He drew one more round of trumps with the jack, then turned to the heart suit. The Mother Superior followed to the ace of hearts but had a decision to make when the king of hearts was played. Should she ruff, taking the chance to make her ♠10? It seemed not. With only diamonds left in her hand, she would have to concede a trick to declarer's queen of diamonds.

The Mother Superior threw a diamond on the heart king and another when the heart queen was played. These cards remained:

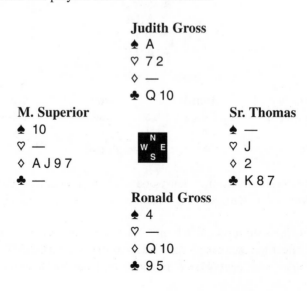

Judith Gross
♠ A
♡ 7 2
◊ —
♣ Q 10

M. Superior
♠ 10
♡ —
◊ A J 9 7
♣ —

Sr. Thomas
♠ —
♡ J
◊ 2
♣ K 8 7

Ronald Gross
♠ 4
♡ —
◊ Q 10
♣ 9 5

Ronald Gross ruffed a heart in his hand and for the fourth time the Mother Superior held on to her ♠10, discarding a diamond. It was the end of the road for declarer. When he played a club to the 10, East won with the king and returned a diamond. Dummy's last trump was forced and West could claim the last two tricks. The game was one down.

'My hand was a bit good, you tell me?' exclaimed Judith Gross. 'You think about a slam and go down in game?'

'Give me two 3-2 breaks and I would make a slam,' her husband replied. 'With everything breaking badly, even game was too high.'

The Mother Superior made no comment but it seemed to her that declarer could have survived the two 4-1 breaks by the strange play of ducking East's jack of clubs at Trick 1. If the defenders took a club ruff, he would be back in control of the hand. On any other return he could ruff a diamond, draw trumps, and score two club tricks by finessing against the king.

The half-time interval was not far away when Sister Grace arrived in a doubled game:

```
Game All                    ♠ K Q J 10 8 2
Dealer North                ♡ A 7 2
                            ◇ Q J 5 3
                            ♣ —

      ♠ A 7 5 4 3                          ♠ 9 6
      ♡ K J 10              N              ♡ Q 8 5
      ◇ A               W       E          ◇ 9 4 2
      ♣ 10 9 7 2             S              ♣ K Q J 8 4

                            ♠ —
                            ♡ 9 6 4 3
                            ◇ K 10 8 7 6
                            ♣ A 6 5 3
```

West	North	East	South
Bill	**Mother of**	**Emily**	**Sister**
Blunkett	**Discipline**	**Blunkett**	**Grace**
-	1♠	2♣	2◇
5♣	5◇	pass	pass
double	all pass		

Bill Blunkett led ♣10 against Five Diamonds doubled and Sister Grace ruffed in the dummy. 'King of spades, please,' she said.

A heart was discarded from the South hand and Blunkett won with the ace. Sister Grace won the jack of hearts switch with dummy's ace and discarded a second heart on the spade queen. When she called for the jack of spades, East ruffed. Declarer overruffed, returned to dummy with a club ruff, and led the ten of spades. The little jig was repeated when East ruffed and South overruffed. This position had been reached:

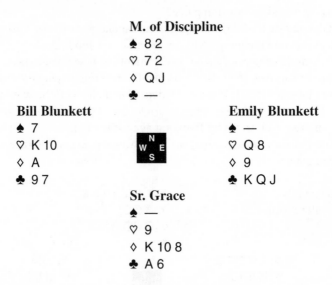

M. of Discipline
- ♠ 8 2
- ♡ 7 2
- ◊ Q J
- ♣ —

Bill Blunkett
- ♠ 7
- ♡ K 10
- ◊ A
- ♣ 9 7

Emily Blunkett
- ♠ —
- ♡ Q 8
- ◊ 9
- ♣ K Q J

Sr. Grace
- ♠ —
- ♡ 9
- ◊ K 10 8
- ♣ A 6

Still showing no inclination to cash the ace of clubs, Sister Grace ruffed her last low club and called for the ♠8. East ruffed, for the third time, and declarer overruffed. Only now did she place the ace of clubs on the table. She made no trick with the card because she ruffed it in dummy. The final move was to play dummy's established ♣2, throwing her last heart. West ruffed with the ace of trumps but no further trick came the defenders' way. The doubled game had been made.

'Well, I can't believe that, Emily,' declared Bill Blunkett. 'You overbid at the two-level and I held twelve points including two aces! How on earth could I expect them to make eleven tricks?'

'They wouldn't have done if you'd led a heart,' his wife replied. 'We had the king, queen and jack between us.'

'If you wanted a heart lead, you shouldn't bid clubs,' Blunkett declared. 'I knew you couldn't have many points so I took your overbid as a lead-director.'

At half-time, with just twelve boards played, the Convent team held a lead of 49 IMPs. The players were ushered into the Blunketts' kitchen for the interval refreshments.

'I've made two cakes,' Emily Blunkett informed them. 'I hope they don't break any of your Convent rules. This one is a chocolate orange cake; the other one is a walnut loaf.'

'Splendid!' exclaimed the Mother Superior. 'How kind of you to bake the cakes yourself.'

'Oh, I don't like buying cakes,' Mrs Blunkett replied. 'You never know what's in them.'

'European Preservative E210 and European colourant E97 probably,' quipped Ronald Gross. 'Everything is dictated by Brussels nowadays.'

Sister Grace smiled politely. 'We've been waiting for them to place some restrictions on our vegetable growing,' she observed. 'Not that anyone in Brussels would know what happens behind the Convent walls. They're two foot thick, you know.'

The second half began with the Mother Superior now facing the Blunketts.

North-South Game
Dealer East

```
                      ♠ K 2
                      ♡ A 7 4
                      ◊ 7 6 2
                      ♣ A 9 7 5 3
  ♠ 9 7 6 4                          ♠ —
  ♡ 8                N              ♡ Q 10 9 5 3
  ◊ 9 8 4         W     E           ◊ A K Q J 3
  ♣ K J 10 4 2        S             ♣ Q 8 6
                      ♠ A Q J 10 8 5 3
                      ♡ K J 6 2
                      ◊ 10 5
                      ♣ —
```

West	North	East	South
Bill	**Sister**	**Emily**	**Mother**
Blunkett	**Thomas**	**Blunkett**	**Superior**
-	-	1♡	4♠
pass	6♣	all pass	

Bill Blunkett led ♡8 and down went the dummy. 'Three good cards for you, Reverend Mother,' announced Sister Thomas. 'I presume your overcall is up to strength, vulnerable against not.'

The Mother Superior inspected the dummy with no great enthusiasm. It was a blessing that she had escaped a diamond lead, of course, and she would now be able to throw one diamond loser on the ace of clubs. Against that, it was by no means clear how she could avoid losing the fourth round of hearts. It could be ruffed in the dummy only if – by some miracle – West held only one trump.

The Mother Superior did not believe in miracles, despite her calling. She won East's queen of hearts with the king and ran the trump suit, hoping that East would come under pressure – real or imaginary. Emily Blunkett, sitting East, parted with three diamonds and one heart. Looking increasingly uncomfortable, she then decided to abandon the club suit. Her trump suit exhausted, the Mother Superior crossed to the ace of hearts. These cards remained:

Sr. Thomas
♠ —
♡ 7
◊ 7
♣ A 10

Bill Blunkett
♠ —
♡ —
◊ 9 8
♣ K J

Emily Blunkett
♠ —
♡ 10 9
◊ A K
♣ —

M. Superior
♠ —
♡ J 6
◊ 10 5
♣ —

The Mother Superior now called for the ace of clubs. Emily Blunkett had seen her partner show out of hearts and knew that she had to retain two cards in that suit. With a small sigh she placed the king of diamonds on the table. The Mother Superior discarded ♡6. 'Small diamond, please,' she said.

The diamond ace appeared from East and the Mother Superior faced her two remaining cards, claiming the contract.

'That won't be very good for us, Bill,' observed Emily Blunkett. 'We needed a diamond lead.'

'Why did you bid *hearts,* then?' Bill Blunkett replied. He reached for his wife's cards and scanned through them in disbelief. 'You should open One Diamond, not One Heart. You were easily strong enough to reverse.'

'Is that right?' queried Emily Blunkett. 'I'm sure Ron Klinger's flipper on opening bids says you should open the higher of two touching suits.'

Her husband smiled at this piece of ignorance. 'Not when you're worth a reversing bid,' he said.

At the other table Ronald Gross occupied the South seat. He had just arrived in a spade game.

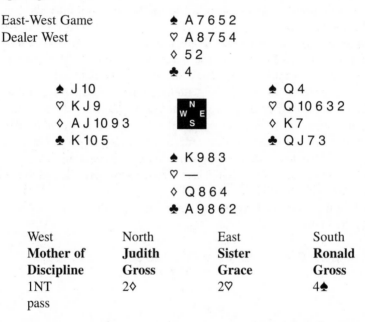

East-West Game
Dealer West

North:
♠ A 7 6 5 2
♡ A 8 7 5 4
◊ 5 2
♣ 4

West:
♠ J 10
♡ K J 9
◊ A J 10 9 3
♣ K 10 5

East:
♠ Q 4
♡ Q 10 6 3 2
◊ K 7
♣ Q J 7 3

South:
♠ K 9 8 3
♡ —
◊ Q 8 6 4
♣ A 9 8 6 2

West	North	East	South
Mother of	**Judith**	**Sister**	**Ronald**
Discipline	**Gross**	**Grace**	**Gross**
1NT	2◊	2♡	4♠
pass			

Judith Gross entered with an Astro overcall, showing spades and another suit. Her husband went all the way to Four Spades and a trump was led.

'Only eight points you have for me?' observed Gross when the dummy went down. 'This will not be easy.'

Judith Gross peered through her gold-rimmed spectacles. 'You would not Astro on this hand?' she demanded. 'With two good five-card majors and two aces, you would not Astro?'

'The shape is fine,' Gross replied. 'Sometimes points are useful too. Play low.'

Declarer won the trump lead with the king. He then cashed the ace of clubs and ruffed a club. What to do now? A crossruff would not work because East's bid had indicated at least five hearts, maybe six. West would overruff. No, he would have to draw another round of trumps. They must be 2-2 after East's queen had not shown at trick 1.

Ronald Gross drew the outstanding trumps with dummy's ace, then ruffed a heart. A club ruff in dummy was followed by another heart ruff, leaving declarer with no more trumps in his hand. Gross shook his head, realising that he was running out of steam. He could ruff a long club good but there would be no way to reach it.

Gross ruffed a club and cashed the ace of hearts. 'You have the rest,' he said. 'Just one down.'

'One down, you say?' queried Judith Gross.

'Seventeen points between us, we had,' Gross replied. 'If anyone had a chance of game it would be them. I was lucky not to be doubled.'

Sister Grace exchanged a glance with the Mother of Discipline. The spade game had surely been cold. If declarer had won the trump lead in dummy, leaving the trump king as an extra entry to the South hand, he could have ruffed the clubs good and enjoyed the long card. It was typical of players at this level to play four or five tricks before they started to make any plan.

'With nine points you should bid just Three Spades,' persisted Judith Gross. 'Plus 140 would be a good score for us.'

Back at the other table the players were drawing their cards for the final board of the match.

North-South Game	♠ A K J 10 9 7	
Dealer South	♡ 10 7 2	
	◊ 7 6 5	
	♣ 9	

♠ 6 5 3		♠ 8 2
♡ —	N W E S	♡ K Q J 9 8 6 5
◊ Q 8 4 3 2		◊ J 10
♣ Q 10 8 7 2		♣ J 3

♠ Q 4
♡ A 4 3
◊ A K 9
♣ A K 6 5 4

West	North	East	South
Bill	**Sister**	**Emily**	**Mother**
Blunkett	**Thomas**	**Blunkett**	**Superior**
-	-	-	2NT
pass	3♡	double	pass
pass	5♠	pass	6♡
pass	6♠	all pass	

The Mother Superior opened 2NT and Sister Thomas responded with a transfer bid. East doubled, to show good hearts, and the Mother Superior passed to indicate only two spades. When Sister Thomas persisted with a slam try, implying at least six trumps, the Mother Superior had visions of a grand slam. Sister Thomas had no such ambitions and signed off hastily at the six level.

A trump was led and the Mother Superior won with the queen. She cashed the ace of clubs and ruffed a club with the nine. She then drew trumps in two more rounds, throwing a heart from her hand.

How did the cards lie? Since West had ignored her partner's lead-directing double in hearts, leading a trump instead, it seemed likely that East held seven hearts alongside her two trumps. The jack of clubs had appeared from East on the second round, so her most likely count was 2-7-2-2.

The Mother Superior gave a thoughtful nod of the head. Yes, in that case a trump squeeze on West should be possible. She played a fourth round of spades, throwing a diamond, then ducked a round of hearts. East won this trick and played back a diamond, won with the ace. These cards remained:

Sr. Thomas
♠ 10
♡ 10 7
♦ 7 6
♣ —

Bill Blunkett
♠ —
♡ —
♦ Q 8
♣ Q 10 8

```
  N
W   E
  S
```

Emily Blunkett
♠ —
♡ K Q J 9
♦ 10
♣ —

M. Superior
♠ —
♡ A
♦ K
♣ K 6 5

63

The king of clubs confirmed that clubs were indeed breaking 5-2. When the Mother Superior continued with the ace of hearts, Bill Blunkett had no good card to play. If he threw a diamond, declarer would cash the king of diamonds and reach dummy with a club ruff to enjoy the established ◊7. He chose instead to discard a club, but the Mother Superior now ruffed a club good for her twelfth trick. The king of diamonds remained as an entry to reach it. 'Just the twelve?' she said, facing her last two cards.

'A heart lead works better,' observed Emily Blunkett. 'I was hoping you might find it after my double.'

'I don't think I had any hearts,' Bill Blunkett replied. 'The ending was rather awkward for me. Perhaps I should have held on to my clubs.'

The Mother Superior smiled sympathetically. 'There was nothing you could do,' she said.

The Convent team had won the 24-board match by an embarrassing 117 IMPs and were soon packed into the Mother Superior's Reinault, heading homewards.

The Mother of Discipline leaned forward from one of the back seats. 'The standard seems to be even worse than in the second division,' she observed. 'They hadn't the first idea about the game.'

'I didn't enjoy winning by such a huge margin at all,' added Sister Thomas. 'We'll have to bring in a weaker pair for the remaining matches, Reverend Mother. Perhaps Sister Myrtle and Sister Benedict would welcome an outing.'

The Mother Superior showed no emotion, continuing to drive at her usual steady 30 mph. 'It's a very kind suggestion, Sister,' she replied. 'It would be a wonderful experience to have teammates such as you and the Mother of Discipline. I'll mention it to them tomorrow.'

VIII

The Mother of Discipline's Expert Defence

The notice board outside the chapel was as cluttered as usual. Monsignor Lucioni from Tewkesbury would be giving a talk on mediaeval systems of irrigation on Thursday, the 21st. Senior choir practice was cancelled this week due to Sister Benedict being away on jury service. By far the most prominent notice, however, boldly inscribed in blue ink, was the following:

Sisters will be proud to hear that the St Hilda's bridge team won their first match in the district league by 117 IMPs. We should all offer our prayers for their continued success in this event.

The Mother of Discipline, who was somewhat late for the Tuesday pairs, glanced towards the notice board. Yes, her notice was still there. How inspired everyone must be feeling! There was nothing like a good first-team result to raise general morale.

Somewhat out of breath, the Mother of Discipline took her seat in the cardroom. She was irritated to find that the first visitors to her table were her least favourite opponents – Sister Theresa and Sister Katherine from the novitiate. Most of the other novices quaked in their shoes when confronted by the Mother of Discipline. These two had never shown her the respect that was due. She was always severe in her selection of punishments, where these two were involved, but it seemed to make no difference.

This was the first board of the round:

```
North-South Game        ♠ —
Dealer East             ♡ Q 10 9 7 6 4
                        ♦ A Q J 6 5
                        ♣ 7 2
    ♠ A K 4                          ♠ J 6
    ♡ J 8 2            N             ♡ A 3
    ♦ 10 9 8 3      W     E          ♦ 7 4 2
    ♣ Q J 3           S             ♣ A K 10 9 5 4
                        ♠ Q 10 9 8 7 5 3 2
                        ♡ K 5
                        ♦ K
                        ♣ 8 6
```

West	North	East	South
Sister	**Sister**	**Mother of**	**Sister**
Grace	**Katherine**	**Discipline**	**Theresa**
-	-	1♣	3♠
double	all pass		

'Negative double, was it?' enquired Sister Theresa.

'At the three level?' exclaimed the Mother of Discipline. 'Of course not. We only play negative doubles up to Two Spades.'

Sister Grace won the first two tricks with the queen and jack of clubs. What next? East could not hold both top hearts, or she would clearly have overtaken in clubs to play them. A heart switch was therefore rather dangerous. Not entirely happy, Sister Grace switched to ♦10.

'Play the ace, Kathie,' said the young declarer.

The Mother of Discipline could not believe what she was hearing. 'Your partner is not a member of some pop group!' she exclaimed. 'Her correct title is Sister Katherine, a fact you may be more inclined to register after saying five Hail Mary's before Compline tonight.' She paused to make a note in her black punishment book.

Sister Theresa dropped ♦K under dummy's ace and played two more top diamonds, throwing both her hearts. Although she could now have reached her hand with a heart ruff, she called for another diamond.

The Mother of Discipline knew what to do to this fourth diamond. She ruffed with the jack, an uppercut aimed at promoting her partner's trump holding.

She sneaked a glance at the young declarer, trying to gauge her reaction. From all appearances the novice had taken it extremely well. She overruffed with the queen and led the ten of trumps from her hand. The defenders ended with just two trumps and two clubs. The contract of Three Spades doubled had been made.

The Mother of Discipline could not hide her irritation. 'Switch to a heart at Trick 3, partner!' she admonished.

'Isn't it easier if you overtake the second club and cash the ace of hearts yourself?' suggested Sister Grace. 'I was worried you might hold the king of hearts instead of the ace.'

The Mother of Discipline was unimpressed by this suggestion. 'We had three side-suit winners and two trump tricks off the top,' she declared. 'It shouldn't be beyond a pair who won their last match by 117 IMPs to take a plus score in those circumstances.'

'You had three trump winners actually, Reverend Mother,' observed Sister Theresa.

'Yes,' said Sister Grace. 'Ruffing with the jack cost a trick, too.'

There was a pregnant pause. 'As the cards lie, you may be right,' replied the Mother of Discipline eventually. 'There are countless situations where the uppercut would gain a trick, though. Every expert defender would take her chance with the jack.'

Sister Grace said no more on the matter. It occurred to her, however, that declarer would hardly have played a fourth diamond if an uppercut could do any damage. She would have returned to hand with a heart ruff.

The Mother of Discipline was hoping for better things as the players drew their cards for the second board of the round.

East-West Game
Dealer South

♠ 82
♥ 963
♦ J862
♣ 7652

♠ 104
♥ J82
♦ A975
♣ 10983

```
  N
W   E
  S
```

♠ AK765
♥ 105
♦ Q103
♣ QJ4

♠ QJ93
♥ AKQ74
♦ K4
♣ AK

West	North	East	South
Sister	**Sister**	**Mother of**	**Sister**
Grace	**Katherine**	**Discipline**	**Theresa**
-	-	-	2♣
pass	2♦	pass	2♥
pass	2NT	pass	3♥
all pass			

Sister Grace led ♣10 and Sister Katherine displayed her almost non-existent dummy.

The Mother of Discipline glared at the novice. 'You don't play that sequence as forcing to game?' she queried.

'No, going via Two Clubs is our only strong sequence,' Sister Katherine replied. 'It has to cover Acol Two hands as well as the game-forcing hands.'

'I thought if you played the Multi you could open Two Hearts with an Acol Two hand?' persisted the Mother of Discipline.

'Can do, Reverend Mother,' replied Sister Katherine, pushing a lock of shiny blonde hair back under her wimple. 'We use it to show hearts and a minor, 6-10 points. It's a more common hand type according to the computer simulations.'

'I've a good mind to ban the Multi in the novitiate,' muttered the Mother of Discipline. 'No point trying to run before you can walk.'

Sister Theresa won the club lead with the ace and led the queen of spades. The Mother of Discipline won with the ace and returned the queen of clubs, won by declarer's king. The jack of spades pinned West's 10 and was taken by the Mother of Discipline's king. Sister Theresa ruffed East's club continuation and drew just two rounds of trumps, leaving this end position:

Sr. Katherine
♠ —
♡ 9
♢ J 8 6 2
♣ 7

Sr. Grace
♠ —
♡ J
♢ A 9 7 5
♣ 9

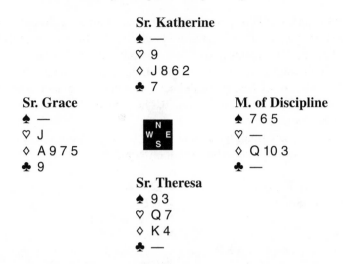

M. of Discipline
♠ 7 6 5
♡ —
♢ Q 10 3
♣ —

Sr. Theresa
♠ 9 3
♡ Q 7
♢ K 4
♣ —

When ♠3 appeared on the table, Sister Grace decided to ruff with the jack ahead of dummy's nine. 'Throw the club,' said Sister Theresa.

A club exit would give a ruff-and-discard, so Sister Grace had to open the diamonds. She scored the diamond ace and declarer then claimed the remainder, making her contract exactly.

The Mother of Discipline swept up her cards and thrust them back into the wallet. Minus 140 did not exactly have the ring of a top about it. 'Isn't it better if you don't ruff that spade, Sister?' she said. 'She ruffs in the dummy and tries a diamond to the king. Now we take the ace and queen of diamonds and I can give you a spade ruff.'

Sister Theresa shook her head at this suggestion. 'I wouldn't come off dummy with a diamond, I'd play a club,' she declared. 'Even if Sister Grace overruffs, it doesn't matter. She would have to play a diamond then.'

'That's right,' said Sister Grace. 'The only way to give the defence a chance is for you to switch to diamonds earlier in the play, Reverend Mother. She's on a guess, then.'

The next few rounds passed by in similar vein. Even the Mother of Discipline had to admit that she was not in the best of form. The final round of the evening brought her to Sister Myrtle's table. She deposited her walking stick against the table and, with some difficulty, lowered herself into the West seat. 'Diabolical that I should have to move,' she declared, in a voice loud enough for the whole room to hear. 'They tell me that no-one can be stationary in a five-and-a-half table movement. I can't see the sense in that.'

The Mother of Discipline gathered her concentration. However modest her score might be, and there was every prospect of it being extremely modest, it would not be disadvantaged by two tops against Sister Myrtle.

'Would you like a mint, Reverend Mother?' asked Sister Myrtle.

The Mother of Discipline delivered a withering glance. Did the woman ever stop eating? 'I have already dined,' she replied. 'I don't believe in snacking between meals.'

'They're very small ones,' said Sister Myrtle. 'You need three or four at a time or you don't get any flavour out of them.'

East-West Game	♠ Q 7 4
Dealer South	♡ K 6
	◇ A K 10 7 5 4
	♣ J 3

	♠ K 10 8 5 2		♠ A J 9 6
	♡ 9 5 3	N	♡ 8 4
	◇ Q 6	W E	◇ J 9
	♣ K 8 2	S	♣ Q 10 7 6 4

	♠ 3
	♡ A Q J 10 7 2
	◇ 8 3 2
	♣ A 9 5

West	North	East	South
Mother of Discipline	**Sister Benedict**	**Sister Grace**	**Sister Myrtle**
-	-	-	1♡
pass	2◇	pass	2♡
pass	3♡	pass	4♡
all pass			

Expecting dummy to hold a fair diamond suit, which might provide some discards, the Mother of Discipline made the attacking lead of a low club. 'You play Three Hearts as forcing?' she exclaimed, when dummy went down with a 13-count.

'I couldn't say if it was forcing or not,' replied Sister Benedict. 'I didn't think she'd pass, anyway.'

The Mother of Discipline raised her eyes to the ceiling. What pleasure could these people possibly gain by playing bridge at such a Neanderthal level?

'I thought it might be useful to keep the bidding low,' continued Sister Benedict, recalling a phrase that she had heard somewhere. 'To leave more room for cue-bidding if partner had a good hand.'

'Ah yes, of course,' grunted the Mother of Discipline. 'The point escaped me.'

Sister Myrtle won the club lead with the ace, then played a diamond to the ace, drawing the six and the nine. After several seconds thought, normally her allocation for an entire evening, she called for the king of diamonds. When both defenders followed, she was able to draw trumps and run the diamond suit, making all thirteen tricks.'

'Oh dear,' exclaimed Sister Benedict. 'Couldn't you make a cue bid? I did keep the bidding nice and low for you.'

'I did think of bidding Four Clubs,' replied Sister Myrtle. 'But that would have been Gerber, of course. It was rather awkward.'

'No need to worry,' said Sister Benedict, brightening considerably as she inspected the scoresheet. Everyone has played in game and only one other pair made thirteen tricks!'

'I'm not surprised,' declared the Mother of Discipline. 'If the second diamond had been ruffed, you'd have gone down in a cold contract.'

Sister Myrtle placed a few more mints in her mouth, sucking on them thoughtfully. What on earth was the MD talking about?

'You should have ducked the club lead,' continued the Mother of Discipline. 'That way you make sure of a club ruff. You still make eleven tricks if the diamonds divide.'

'But I was sure the diamonds would be 2-2,' protested Sister Myrtle.

The Mother of Discipline's tolerance was exhausted. 'Since when does a 40% chance qualify as a certainty?' she demanded. 'The remaining 60% of the time you would have gone down.'

'The six and the nine appeared on the first round of diamonds, Reverend Mother,' exclaimed Sister Myrtle. 'That meant I could rule out all the 4-0 breaks and all the 3-1 breaks where an honour was singleton.'

Sister Benedict nodded supportively. 'Very sound,' she muttered.

'And if your six of diamonds was a singleton,' continued Sister Myrtle, 'you would surely have led it.'

'Very impressive reasoning, partner,' declared Sister Benedict.

'With queen-jack-one you would obviously have split your honours,' concluded Sister Myrtle, 'so, as I said, the chance of a 2-2 break was 100%.'

The Mother of Discipline shook her head disdainfully, but it seemed that there was an element of truth to Sister Myrtle's ramblings. Perhaps she should have dropped the queen of diamonds on the first round. There was nothing to lose by it.

The Mother of Discipline drew her cards for the last board of the round, determined to end the evening with a good score.

Game All	♠ A K Q J 8 7		
Dealer North	♡ 10 3		
	◊ A J 4		
	♣ 7 4		

♠ 9 6 2		♠ 10 3
♡ A J 5	N W E S	♡ K 8 7 4 2
◊ 9 8 6		◊ K 5 3 2
♣ A 9 6 5		♣ J 10

♠ 5 4	
♡ Q 9 6	
◊ Q 10 7	
♣ K Q 8 3 2	

West	North	East	South
Mother of	**Sister**	**Sister**	**Sister**
Discipline	**Benedict**	**Grace**	**Myrtle**
-	1♠	pass	1NT
pass	3♠	pass	3NT
all pass			

Sister Grace won the ◊8 lead with the king and switched to ♡4. The Mother of Discipline won with the jack and cashed the ace of hearts, her partner playing ♡2 to proclaim an initial five cards in the suit.

The Mother of Discipline was not to be rushed with her defence. If East held the king of hearts the defenders could cash three more winners in the suit. It was entirely possible, however, that East held the queen of hearts and declarer the king. In that case the only chance of beating the contract was to find partner with ♣K. The solution was obvious. Rather than gamble on the heart position immediately, she should cash the ace of clubs. Partner's signal would then tell her what to do.

The Mother of Discipline cashed the ace of clubs, noting the 10 from her partner. Nodding her head in expert fashion, she continued with a second club. A surprised Sister Myrtle won the trick and, somewhat apologetically, claimed the remainder. The game had been made.

'We had seven tricks to take, didn't we?' said Sister Grace.

'I can't help that,' declared the Mother of Discipline. 'My defence catered for you holding either king. I needed a signal from you in clubs to tell me which king you held.'

'Yes, but I only had the jack and ten of clubs,' replied Sister Grace. 'I couldn't give you a low club.'

The Mother of Discipline had heard enough. 'It's one of those annoying hands where a beginner would do well and an expert wouldn't,' she declared. 'It's a cross one has to bear.'

'Perhaps it's better if you cash the ace of clubs before the ace of hearts,' suggested Sister Grace. 'Then if I have the club king and my hearts are queen-high I can throw the queen of hearts under your ace to force you to switch back to clubs.'

'I've never heard of anything so convoluted,' grunted the Mother of Discipline. 'I don't want to rely on you making extravagant queen discards when a simple signal is available. No, an international player such as Sandra Landy would have defended in exactly the same way that I did. I'm sure of it.'

It seemed to Sister Grace that her partner had missed an inference from declarer's play. If she held the king of hearts, and was missing the two top clubs, she would surely have risen with the king when a heart was played through. To play low would risk the immediate loss of two hearts, one diamond and two clubs.

'Landy and I are probably the only defenders in the country capable of defending so well on the hand,' continued the Mother of Discipline, rising slowly to her feet. 'I dare say I'm exaggerating a bit, but you'd certainly need years of experience before scoring a bottom on that board.'

IX

The Martyr's Platter

Every year, in the week before Lent, St Hilda's played a 32-board match against the St Titus Monastery. At stake was the Martyr's Platter, a 14th century relic of worm-ridden oak, rimmed with silver. In the forty years since the inauguration of the event, the Convent had been victorious on some sixteen occasions. In the past decade they had achieved a good edge, however, and the Mother Superior was determined that they should achieve another success. 'The Abbot is their weak link, of course,' she instructed her teammates. 'We must apply the maximum pressure when playing against him.'

The match, staged this year at St Hilda's, started promptly at two o'clock. The first set placed the two captains in opposition.

'We made a very good start last year,' declared the Mother Superior. 'Didn't we win the first set by 51 IMPs to 7?'

Abbot Hugo Yorke-Smith, a large bald-headed man, smiled at this. 'Lightning does sometimes strike twice in the same place,' he replied. 'I don't expect it will on this occasion.'

'I certainly hope not,' continued the Mother Superior. 'The rest of last year's match was rather an anti-climax.'

This was the first deal:

```
East-West Game          ♠ 10 4 3
Dealer South            ♡ K Q 8 3
                        ◊ A 5
                        ♣ K 7 6 2
        ♠ K 8 5                         ♠ J 9
        ♡ 10 9 7 4         N            ♡ J 2
        ◊ J 8 3        W       E        ◊ K 10 7 6 2
        ♣ Q 9 4            S            ♣ J 10 8 3
                        ♠ A Q 7 6 2
                        ♡ A 6 5
                        ◊ Q 9 4
                        ♣ A 5
```

West	North	East	South
The	**Sister**	**Brother**	**Mother**
Abbot	**Thomas**	**Xavier**	**Superior**
-	-	-	1♠
pass	2♣	pass	2NT
pass	3♠	pass	4♣
pass	4◊	pass	6♠
all pass			

The Abbot led ♡10 and down went the dummy. The Mother Superior raised an alarmed eyebrow. What a terrible slam! She hadn't overbid herself. It was entirely Sister Thomas's fault; she had no right to cue-bid the diamond ace with only twelve points and three trumps to the 10. The Mother of Discipline would doubtless point this out in no uncertain terms, should the slam go down.

The Mother Superior won the heart lead with dummy's king and finessed the queen of trumps. The Abbot won with the king and played a second heart, hoping that his partner's ♡2 on the first round proclaimed a singleton. Declarer captured East's jack with the ace and played the ace of trumps, pleased to see the jack fall from East. She took the marked finesse of dummy's ♡8, drew West's last trump with the 10, and discarded a diamond on the heart queen. A club to the ace left this position:

Sr. Thomas
♠ —
♡ —
◊ A 5
♣ K 7 6

The Abbot
♠ —
♡ —
◊ J 8 3
♣ Q 9

```
    N
  W   E
    S
```

Bro. Xavier
♠ —
♡ —
◊ K 10
♣ J 10 8

M. Superior
♠ 7 6
♡ —
◊ Q 9
♣ 5

When the Mother Superior led her penultimate trump, throwing a diamond from dummy, East was caught in a trump squeeze. He threw a diamond, hoping that his partner held the queen, but it was not to be. Declarer crossed to the ace of diamonds, felling East's king, cashed the king of clubs and ruffed a club to her hand. She then faced her last card – the good queen of diamonds. The slam had been made.

'Not the best, Abbot,' declared Brother Xavier. 'The heart lead gave them a trick in that suit and we needed a diamond switch when you were in with the trump king.'

'Do you *ever* accept the blame when a hand goes wrong?' demanded the Abbot. 'Make the obvious double of the 4◊ cue-bid and I'd lead a diamond at Trick 1. There's no chance at all, then.'

At the other table the Mother of Discipline and Sister Grace faced St Titus's top pair, Brother Lucius and the Italian monk, Brother Paulo.

'You're looking very bronzed, Paulo,' said Sister Grace. 'Been back to Tuscany recently, have you?'

Brother Paulo smiled broadly. 'Yes, yes, I go back one month a year as always,' he replied. 'You think the sun-tan is improving my good looks?'

Sister Grace laughed. 'That would scarcely be possible, would it?' she said.

The Mother of Discipline peered disapprovingly at her partner. Even in jest, such flirtatious behaviour was unacceptable. 'Shall we play?' she said.

The players drew their cards for this board:

East-West Game
Dealer West

```
                    ♠ A 7 4
                    ♡ 9 3
                    ◇ A 10 8 5
                    ♣ A K 7 6
   ♠ K 8 2                           ♠ 10
   ♡ A K 6          N                ♡ Q 10 8 5 2
   ◇ J 9 7 2      W   E              ◇ K Q 6 4
   ♣ J 8 3          S                ♣ Q 10 2
                    ♠ Q J 9 6 5 3
                    ♡ J 7 4
                    ◇ 3
                    ♣ 9 5 4
```

West	North	East	South
Sister	**Brother**	**Mother of**	**Brother**
Grace	**Paulo**	**Discipline**	**Lucius**
1NT	double	2♡	2♠
pass	pass	3◇	3♠
pass	4♠	double	all pass

Sister Grace and her partner favoured the weak notrump at all vulnerabilities. On the present West hand, with its nine losers, many would have baulked at such a bid. Not Sister Grace. 'You either believe in the weak notrump or you don't,' was her oft expressed opinion.

A competitive auction ensued and the silver-haired Brother Lucius ended in Four Spades doubled. Sister Grace led the ace of hearts, followed by the king. After a short pause she continued with a third round of hearts, hoping to promote her king of trumps by forcing the dummy to ruff. Brother Lucius ruffed in the dummy, cashed the ace of diamonds, and ruffed a diamond. He then ran the queen of trumps, dropping the 10 from East. Barring a somewhat unlikely false card from East, West's trump king was now immune from capture. There was also a loser in the club suit. What could be done?

Brother Lucius crossed to the ace of clubs and ruffed another diamond. A club to the king came next, followed by a third diamond ruff. The lead was in the South hand and these cards were still to be played:

Bro. Paulo
♠ A
♡ —
♢ —
♣ 7 6

Sr. Grace
♠ K 8
♡ —
♢ —
♣ J

```
  N
W   E
  S
```

M. of Discipline
♠ —
♡ 10 5
♢ —
♣ Q

Bro. Lucius
♠ J 9
♡ —
♢ —
♣ 9

When Brother Lucius led a club, the Mother of Discipline had to win with the queen. The enforced heart return then guillotined West's king of trumps. Whether or not she overruffed declarer's ♠9, the doubled game would be made.

'Difficult for you, Reverend Mother,' observed Sister Grace. 'If you happen to unblock the queen of clubs, I can win the third club over here and play a trump to the bare ace. I make my king of trumps then.'

The Mother of Discipline waved this suggestion aside. 'I'd look pretty silly throwing the queen of clubs if declarer held the jack,' she replied.

Sister Grace was not one to press the matter. It occurred to her, however, that she was marked with the jack of clubs on the bidding. Eight points in the red suits and three for the trump king; that came to just 11. To make up a 1NT opening, even by her standards, she would have to hold the club jack too.

Back at the other table the Mother Superior had arrived in a tricky 3NT contract.

North-South Game
Dealer South

```
                ♠ 6 5
                ♥ A J 6 3
                ◇ 9 8 5 3
                ♣ K 8 5
♠ A 10 8 7 3 2              ♠ 9 4
♥ 8 4          N           ♥ 10 9 7 5 2
◇ K Q 4      W   E         ◇ J
♣ 10 4          S          ♣ A 9 6 3 2
                ♠ K Q J
                ♥ K Q
                ◇ A 10 7 6 2
                ♣ Q J 7
```

West	North	East	South
The	**Sister**	**Brother**	**Mother**
Abbot	**Thomas**	**Xavier**	**Superior**
-	-	-	1◇
1♠	double	pass	3NT
all pass			

The Abbot led ♠7 against 3NT and the Mother Superior won with the jack. All would be easy if diamonds were 2-2, so she continued with ace and another diamond. The Abbot won the second round with the queen and East showed out, throwing a heart. When the Abbot cleared the spades, playing ace and another, Brother Xavier could not afford to throw a second heart. He discarded a club and the trick was won by South's king.

The Mother Superior surveyed her remaining assets thoughtfully. For the contract to have any chance, East would have to hold the club ace. He would doubtless hold up on the first two rounds, to avoid setting up dummy's king as an entry to the blocked hearts. But... yes, the contract could still be made!

The Mother Superior continued with ♣Q, which was allowed to win. She unblocked the king and queen of hearts and played ♣J. Brother Xavier let this card win, too, but it brought him no relief. Down to ♥109 ♣A9, he was thrown in with a club. After cashing ♣9, he had to give the last two tricks to the dummy. The notrump game had been made.

'You played it well,' said Brother Xavier.

'Nothing much to it,' replied the Mother Superior. 'It can hardly be other than a flat board.'

Meanwhile, Brother Lucius had arrived in a different notrump game.

Game All   ♠ A Q J 3
Dealer South   ♡ Q 2
                   ♢ K 10 8 7 2
                   ♣ 6 3

♠ 10 6 2		♠ 8 5 4
♡ 9 5 3	N	♡ A 8 6 4
♢ A 9 6 3	W E	♢ Q 5
♣ K 8 5	S	♣ J 10 9 2

                  ♠ K 9 7
                  ♡ K J 10 7
                  ♢ J 4
                  ♣ A Q 7 4

West	North	East	South
Sister	**Brother**	**Mother of**	**Brother**
Grace	**Paulo**	**Discipline**	**Lucius**
-	-	-	1NT
pass	2♣	pass	2♡
pass	3NT	all pass	

Sister Grace led ♢3, recoiling somewhat when dummy went down with a five-card diamond suit. 'Nice hand, Paulo,' said Brother Lucius.

Most players would have called immediately for a low card from dummy. Brother Lucius paused to consider the matter, however. If East won with the diamond queen and switched to the jack or ten of clubs, the contract would be at risk. How about rising with dummy's king of diamonds? He would be in the same position if East won with the ace and switched to clubs, so maybe it was a 50-50 guess as to which diamond honour East held. No, that wasn't so, of course. If he rose with the king and the card won, the contract could be guaranteed by clearing the hearts. If instead he played a low diamond and this forced the ace, the contract would not be guaranteed. East might still beat the contract by switching to clubs. 'King, please,' said Brother Lucius.

Dummy's king of diamonds won the trick and Lucius continued with the queen of hearts. He could not be prevented from scoring four spades, three hearts and one trick in each minor. The contract was his.

'Good move at Trick 1,' congratulated Brother Paulo.

Sister Grace nodded. 'It must be the right play,' she said. 'If East has the ace it doesn't help you very much to play low.'

'Exactly,' replied Brother Lucius.

The half-time interval was approaching when the Mother Superior arrived in a notrump slam. This was the deal:

East-West Game
Dealer West

```
                 ♠ A K Q J 7 6 5
                 ♡ —
                 ♦ A 7 6 3
                 ♣ 5 2
    ♠ 10                              ♠ 9 4
    ♡ J 5               N             ♡ Q 10 9 7 6 4 3 2
    ♦ Q 10 8        W       E         ♦ J 4
    ♣ A Q J 10 9 4 3    S             ♣ 8
                 ♠ 8 3 2
                 ♡ A K 8
                 ♦ K 9 5 2
                 ♣ K 7 6
```

West	North	East	South
The	**Sister**	**Brother**	**Mother**
Abbot	**Thomas**	**Xavier**	**Superior**
3♣	4♠	pass	4NT
pass	5♣	pass	6NT
all pass			

The Mother Superior's 4NT was for Roman Key-card Blackwood. The response showed three of the five 'aces', the king of trumps counting as an ace. It was no good bidding the slam in spades because East would then be able to lead through the club king. 'Six Notrumps,' she said.

The Abbot led ♣10 and down went the dummy. 'I thought I had a chance of playing the hand when I picked up this spade suit,' observed Sister Thomas.

The Mother Superior smiled. 'I'm not one to grab all the hands, you know that,' she replied. 'Play the spade ace, will you?'

Prospects were not good. There were eleven tricks on top and a twelfth would have to come from some sort of squeeze. If West's shape were 2-2-2-7, East would hold the sole guard on both red suits. It would not be possible to rectify the count, but on the last spade East would have to throw his singleton club to retain both red-suit guards. Yes, she could then surrender a diamond to set up the twelfth trick.

When the Mother Superior played a second round of spades, West showed out. Unless he had an unlikely 8-card suit for his club pre-empt, a red-suit squeeze on East was no longer possible. It seemed that the only remaining chance was to play West for the diamond guard.

The Mother Superior ran dummy's spade winners, then crossed to the king of diamonds and played the ace of hearts. These cards remained:

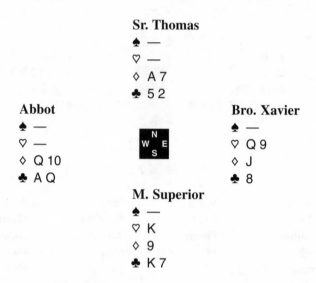

Sr. Thomas
- ♠ —
- ♡ —
- ◊ A 7
- ♣ 5 2

Abbot
- ♠ —
- ♡ —
- ◊ Q 10
- ♣ A Q

Bro. Xavier
- ♠ —
- ♡ Q 9
- ◊ J
- ♣ 8

M. Superior
- ♠ —
- ♡ K
- ◊ 9
- ♣ K 7

When the king of hearts was played, the Abbot had no card to spare. If he threw the club queen, declarer would dispense with dummy's ◊7, then duck a club. The Abbot eventually threw ◊10, on the off chance that declarer's last three cards were ♣K87. No such luck was forthcoming. The Mother Superior discarded a club from dummy and scored the slam-going tricks with the ace and seven of diamonds.

'Bit heavy for a pre-empt, weren't you?' observed the Mother Superior. 'If you open 1♣, it might be more difficult to reach the slam.'

The Abbot could summon no enthusiasm for discussing the bidding. Even with that mad overbidder, Brother Paulo, at the other table, there was no guarantee that the board would be flat. 'A vulnerable pre-empt indicates a fair hand,' he declared. 'I expect your West player will do the same.'

The first half soon drew to a close. There had been a large number of swings in both directions and St Hilda's held a lead of just 5 IMPs.

'Time for tea, everyone!' called the Mother Superior.

The Abbot's spirits rose somewhat. Life might be hard but it did have its compensations.

X

The Abbot's Missed Slam

' I hear that you now have an Internet site for St. Titus,' said the Mother Superior.

'Yes, indeed,' replied the Abbot, finding room for just one more buttered scone on his tea plate. 'Last week we managed to set up a secure interface for credit-card donations.'

'I wonder if you'd mind having a brief chat with young Sister Theresa, our computer expert,' continued the Mother Superior. 'Our two establishments being in the same business, as it were, we'd be most grateful for any tips you could pass on.'

Noting that there was only one syrup flapjack remaining, the Abbot stretched out an arm in that direction. 'I didn't set it all up personally, you understand,' he said. 'She will need to get in touch with Brother Cameron. I believe his email address is, er... brocam@titus.com.uk. Let me write it down for you on the back of your scorecard.'

The second half of the match for the Martyr's Platter saw the Mother Superior and Sister Thomas taking on Brother Lucius and Brother Paulo. This was an early board:

Game All   ♠ A 4 3
Dealer North   ♡ 5 4
                   ◊ A K 4 2
                   ♣ J 6 3 2

♠ 8 7 6		♠ 9 2
♡ 10 9 8 3	N W E S	♡ A K J 6 2
◊ 8 5		◊ Q 10 9 7 6
♣ K 10 9 7		♣ 5

                   ♠ K Q J 10 5
                   ♡ Q 7
                   ◊ J 3
                   ♣ A Q 8 4

West	North	East	South
Brother	**Sister**	**Brother**	**Mother**
Lucius	**Thomas**	**Paulo**	**Superior**
-	1NT	2♣	3♠
pass	4♠	all pass	

Brother Paulo entered the auction with an Apstro 2♣, showing hearts and another suit. The Mother Superior was soon in Four Spades and West led ♡10. Brother Paulo cashed two heart winners, declarer's queen falling on the second round, then switched to his singleton club.

The Mother Superior paused for a moment. Was it possible that clubs was East's other suit? It seemed unlikely. In any case, if East held four clubs rather than five she might still succeed by rising with the ace. If West's singleton was the king, ten or nine, she would lose only one trick in the suit.

The Mother Superior rose with the ace of clubs, then drew two rounds of trumps with the king and queen. Both defenders followed and her next move was a low club towards dummy's jack. Brother Lucius could not afford to rise with the king or declarer would escape for just one club loser. He played the nine and dummy's jack won the trick, East throwing a heart.

'Small diamond, please,' said the Mother Superior.

Brother Paulo went in with the queen, winning the trick. Declarer's diamond winners were blocked but since East had no trump to play, the entry needed to unblock the diamonds was inviolate. When Brother Paulo returned another diamond, the Mother Superior won with the jack and crossed to dummy with a trump to the ace. 'My last two clubs go on the diamond ace-king,' she announced.

Brother Lucius could recognise a piece of good dummy play when he saw one. 'You timed it well,' he observed. 'Of course, with our noble leader being South at the other table it will surely be a flat board.'

The Mother Superior smiled at this. 'I only hope that my own teammates display such faith in their captain,' she replied. 'There wasn't much to it, really. I could hardly risk running the club.'

Meanwhile, at the other table, the Abbot faced Sister Grace, a distant cousin of his. He arrived in a slam on this board:

```
Game All          ♠ K 5
Dealer North      ♡ K Q 8 7 4 2
                  ◊ 8 3 2
                  ♣ K 7

  ♠ J 7 4 2                      ♠ 10 9 6 3
  ♡ A 9 6           N            ♡ J 10 5 3
  ◊ K 10 7 4      W   E          ◊ 9 6
  ♣ J 3             S            ♣ 9 8 4

                  ♠ A Q 8
                  ♡ —
                  ◊ A Q J 5
                  ♣ A Q 10 6 5 2
```

West	North	East	South
Mother of	**Brother**	**Sister**	**The**
Discipline	**Xavier**	**Grace**	**Abbot**
-	1♡	pass	3♣
pass	3♡	pass	4♣
pass	5♣	pass	6♣
all pass			

The Mother of Discipline favoured attacking leads against a small slam. She led ◊4 and the Abbot won in hand with the queen. With any luck there would be no loser in the trump suit. What could be done in diamonds, though? Ah yes, he could discard one of dummy's diamonds on a spade, then take a diamond ruff. 'King of spades, please,' he said, adopting his most expert tone.

'You're in hand,' said the Mother of Discipline.

The Abbot gave an irritated shake of the head. What on earth did it matter which hand he was in when he was cashing a winner? After a spade to the king he returned to the diamond ace and cashed two more spades, throwing a diamond. The stage was now set for a diamond ruff. West followed with the 10 on the third round, so East was known to be out of the suit. 'Ruff with the king,' instructed the Abbot.

East discarded a spade and the Abbot now returned to hand with a heart ruff, to ruff his last diamond with the seven. East overruffed with the eight but when the Abbot regained the lead he was able to draw the outstanding trumps in two rounds. Twelve tricks were his.

The Abbot beamed happily, turning towards Sister Grace. 'I had to ruff the third diamond high,' he explained. 'Otherwise you can overruff and return a trump.'

It seemed to Sister Grace that the hand had been entirely misplayed. After a diamond lead into the ace-queen declarer could simply have discarded his remaining diamond losers on dummy's king-queen of hearts, losing just one heart trick.

The Abbot reached happily for his scorecard. 'I expect most players at our level would find the right line,' he said.

Quite so, thought Sister Grace. Not you, of course, but most players would. A hand or two later, the Abbot arrived in a heart game.

North-South Game	♠ 10 8 3
Dealer South	♡ A 6
	◊ A 9 6 5
	♣ A 10 7 4

♠ A K 7 6	♠ J 9 5 2
♡ 7 5 4 3 2	♡ —
◊ Q 4	◊ J 10 8
♣ J 6	♣ K Q 9 8 3 2

	♠ Q 4
	♡ K Q J 10 9 8
	◊ K 7 3 2
	♣ 5

West	North	East	South
Mother of	**Brother**	**Sister**	**The**
Discipline	**Xavier**	**Grace**	**Abbot**
-	-	-	1♡
pass	2♣	pass	2♡
pass	4♡	all pass	

The Mother of Discipline led the ace of spades against Four Hearts. When dummy appeared, she continued with two more rounds of the suit. The Abbot ruffed the third spade, observing that there seemed to be little interest in the hand. To escape for one diamond loser he would need to find the suit 3-2, or East with a singleton honour. At Trick 4 he crossed to the ace of trumps, not overjoyed to see East showing out.

The Abbot paused to take stock of the situation. If he simply drew trumps at this stage, he would exhaust his own trumps in the process. He would then have no protection against the spade suit when he conceded a trick in diamonds. It seemed that he would have to set up the diamond suit immediately, while dummy's ♥6 offered some protection against a fourth round of spades. It occurred to him that if East held five spades he would rather have had the ace of trumps in dummy. He could then have overruffed West if East led a fourth round of spades. Had he foreseen a 5-0 trump break, he would have cashed the first round of trumps in his hand instead.

At Trick 5 the Abbot led a low diamond from dummy, the jack appearing from East. If East had started with five spades, not unlikely with trumps being 5-0 the other way, the Abbot could not afford her to gain the lead. He therefore won the trick with the king. The Mother of Discipline was aware of the Abbot's difficulties. Mindful of her earlier failure to unblock a queen, she contributed the queen on the first round of diamonds. The Abbot now played a second round of diamonds, the four appearing from West. To duck this to East would lead to an immediate diamond ruff, so the Abbot called for dummy's ace. These cards remained:

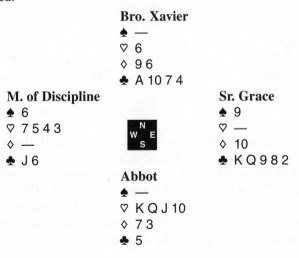

Bro. Xavier
♠ —
♥ 6
◇ 9 6
♣ A 10 7 4

M. of Discipline
♠ 6
♥ 7 5 4 3
◇ —
♣ J 6

Sr. Grace
♠ 9
♥ —
◇ 10
♣ K Q 9 8 2

Abbot
♠ —
♥ K Q J 10
◇ 7 3
♣ 5

When the Abbot played another diamond, East won with the 10 and the Mother of Discipline discarded her last spade. A fourth round of spades from East then killed the contract. If the Abbot ruffed in his own hand he would lose a trump trick by length. He chose to discard, in fact, but West now scored her seven of trumps in front of dummy's six. The game was one down.

'Unfortunate trump break,' observed Brother Xavier. 'Was there anything you could do?'

The Abbot suddenly felt very tired. The fifty-mile drive to the match, the stress of captaincy – all these things took their toll. 'I've no idea,' he replied. 'I'm certainly not going to spend ages at the start of each hand, planning what to do against some 1% distribution.'

At the other table the Mother Superior had just arrived in Four Spades.

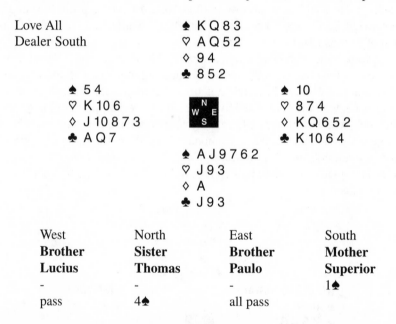

Love All
Dealer South

```
                ♠ K Q 8 3
                ♡ A Q 5 2
                ◇ 9 4
                ♣ 8 5 2
  ♠ 5 4                          ♠ 10
  ♡ K 10 6          N            ♡ 8 7 4
  ◇ J 10 8 7 3   W     E         ◇ K Q 6 5 2
  ♣ A Q 7          S             ♣ K 10 6 4
                ♠ A J 9 7 6 2
                ♡ J 9 3
                ◇ A
                ♣ J 9 3
```

West	North	East	South
Brother	**Sister**	**Brother**	**Mother**
Lucius	**Thomas**	**Paulo**	**Superior**
-	-	-	1♠
pass	4♠	all pass	

Brother Lucius led ◇J, won in the South hand. The Mother Superior drew trumps in two rounds, then ruffed dummy's last diamond. When she exited with a low club, East won with the 10 and returned the suit. The Mother Superior played the jack from her hand and Brother Lucius paused for thought before playing to the trick. If he won with the queen and cashed the ace, he would then have to open the heart suit – disastrous if declarer held the jack. How did the club suit lie? If declarer held the king and jack of clubs, she would surely have led clubs twice from the dummy. Yes, it was a near certainty that Paulo held the king of clubs!

His mind made up, Brother Lucius won the second round of clubs with the ace and exited with the club queen. Paulo overtook with the king and switched to ♡8. The Mother Superior tried her luck with the nine but Lucius covered with the 10. Dummy's queen won the trick but when the king failed to drop on the next round the game was one down.

'Nothing I could do unless they helped me,' said the Mother Superior. 'Perhaps a raise to Three Spades was enough on your hand.'

'I'm not staying out of game on a seven-loser hand,' Sister Thomas replied. 'You were a bit light yourself, weren't you?'

The hard-fought match was drawing to a close when the Abbot arrived in 3NT on this board:

```
Game All              ♠ 8 6 3
Dealer North          ♡ K Q 10 3
                      ◇ A 7
                      ♣ K Q 10 4
      ♠ A Q 9 5 2                    ♠ K 7
      ♡ 9 8 5          N             ♡ 7 6 2
      ◇ 8 6 2        W   E           ◇ 10 5 4 3
      ♣ 8 7            S             ♣ 9 6 5 2
                      ♠ J 10 4
                      ♡ A J 4
                      ◇ K Q J 9
                      ♣ A J 3
```

West	North	East	South
Mother of	**Brother**	**Sister**	**The**
Discipline	**Xavier**	**Grace**	**Abbot**
-	1♣	pass	2NT
pass	3NT	all pass	

The St Titus pair used a strong 1NT when vulnerable, so Brother Xavier opened 1♣. When the Abbot responded with a Baron 2NT, Xavier showed his hand type by rebidding 3NT. The Abbot had nothing more to say, on his minimum Baron hand, and this became the final contract. The Mother of Discipline led ♣5 and the Convent pair soon had five tricks before them.

The Abbot thrust his cards back into the wallet. 'It's the sort of absurd bidding challenge hand where they say you should bid Four Hearts,' he declared. 'Not that anyone would, except in a bidding challenge.'

'It could be a lucky one for us, even so,' said Sister Grace. 'Our pair play a weak notrump throughout, so North should be the declarer in 3NT.'

The Mother of Discipline looked triumphantly towards the Abbot. 'Not so easy to find a spade lead from king doubleton,' she observed.

The Convent team soon reconvened for the final comparison. 'Did you play Board 32 the right way round?' asked the Mother of Discipline. 'You opened 1NT on the North cards, did you?'

'Unfortunately not,' replied the Mother Superior. 'Sister Thomas looked favourably on the two tens and opened 1♣, treating the hand as a 15-count.'

The Mother of Discipline winced. Did Sister Thomas have to overbid *every* hand? 'So now you played notrumps from the South hand, I suppose?'

'I'm afraid so,' replied the Mother Superior. 'Let's score, anyway.'

A few IMPs went backwards and forwards as the first seven boards of the set were scored. 'And, flat board, plus 100 on the last one,' said the Mother of Discipline. 'What does that come to? It's going to be very close; I don't like the look of it.'

The Mother Superior was looking pleased with herself. 'The last board wasn't flat, actually,' she said. 'We scored plus 1440. With a strong notrump facing my Baron 2NT response, I didn't like to play in less than a slam.'

The Mother of Discipline's mouth fell open. 'They didn't lead a spade?' she exclaimed.

'Against 6NT? Of course not!' replied the Mother of Discipline. 'Brother Lucius was on lead and he led a safe heart. I claimed twelve tricks the moment the dummy went down.'

It was the duty of the losing captain to present the Martyr's Platter to the winning captain. 'Well done,' said the Abbot, barely managing to get the words out as he handed over the trophy. What a travesty of justice! Fancy losing by just 2 IMPs after a final board like that.

'Thank you, Abbot,' said the Mother Superior, raising the platter above her head in a mock-triumphant gesture. 'It was an excellent match and it could have gone either way. Still, the side that makes the most of the slam hands usually wins in the end!'

XI

The Mother of Discipline's Big Catch

It had been a tiresome session and the Mother of Discipline was looking every one of her 82 years old as she drew her cards for the final hand of the weekly Convent pairs. This was the deal:

East-West Game
Dealer South

North
♠ J 9 7 2
♥ 8 6 5 4
♦ A 4
♣ Q 9 2

West
♠ 6 3
♥ K Q J 9
♦ 8 6 5
♣ J 8 6 3

East
♠ 8 4
♥ 3
♦ Q J 10 3 2
♣ A K 10 7 5

South
♠ A K Q 10 5
♥ A 10 7 2
♦ K 9 7
♣ 4

West	North	East	South
Sister	**Sister**	**Mother of**	**Sister**
Grace	**Carol**	**Discipline**	**Colleen**
-	-	-	1♠
pass	2♠	2NT	4♠
all pass			

Sister Colleen arrived in Four Spades after the Mother of Discipline had intervened with an Unusual 2NT. The king of hearts was led and the young declarer won with the ace. What could be done? East's ♡3 at Trick 1 made it a near certainty that hearts were 4-1. It seemed that she was destined to lose three hearts and one club.

Sister Colleen drew just one round of trumps, then played the ace and king of diamonds, followed by a diamond ruff. A trump to her hand revealed a 2-2 break in the suit, confirming also that hearts were divided 4-1. These cards remained:

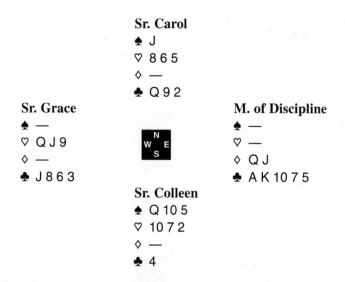

Sr. Carol
♠ J
♡ 8 6 5
◇ —
♣ Q 9 2

Sr. Grace
♠ —
♡ Q J 9
◇ —
♣ J 8 6 3

M. of Discipline
♠ —
♡ —
◇ Q J
♣ A K 10 7 5

Sr. Colleen
♠ Q 10 5
♡ 10 7 2
◇ —
♣ 4

Sister Colleen now led a club, calling for dummy's nine. The Mother of Discipline won with the 10 and continued with the ace of clubs. Declarer declined to ruff the trick, preferring to throw a heart. When the king of clubs was played, she threw another heart. The Mother of Discipline had reached the end of the road. The lead of any of her four remaining cards would concede a ruff-and-discard. When she played a fourth round of clubs, Sister Colleen discarded the last heart from her hand and ruffed in the dummy. Ten tricks were hers.

'Well played, partner,' said Sister Carol, inspecting the scoresheet. 'No-one else seems to have made it.'

'Let me see that,' snapped the Mother of Discipline. She scanned the scoresheet with a look of amazement. 'One disgraceful 1100 in Five Clubs doubled, two 140s and six minus 50s. Would you believe it? The standard of dummy play in the Convent is deplorable nowadays.'

Sister Grace leaned forward mischievously. 'Perhaps you should speak to all the declarers who went down?' she suggested. 'Impose some sort of penance on those who misplayed it.'

Such witticisms always passed over the head of the Mother of Discipline. She reached for her black Punishment Book and made a note of the offending pairs.

Later that evening Sister Grace was enjoying a cup of cocoa in the Mother Superior's study. 'What did you do on Board 19, Reverend Mother?' she enquired.

The Mother Superior consulted her scorecard. 'I went one down in Four Spades,' she replied. 'A club loser and three unavoidable heart losers, if I remember rightly.'

Sister Grace smiled to herself. She could just imagine the Mother of Discipline posting one of her usual notices.

The South players of Pairs 2, 5, 7, 8, 12 and 16 will report to my study directly after Lauds tomorrow.

She would find an unusually large fish in her net if she did.

'I must be confusing it with another board, Reverend Mother,' declared Sister Grace, pouring herself another mug of cocoa. 'On the spade game I had in mind declarer didn't lose any heart tricks at all.'

XII

Sister Myrtle's Brilliancy

'They're not so tasty as they used to be,' declared Sister Myrtle, tossing a couple of licorice allsorts into her mouth. 'When I was a young girl, licorice wasn't rock hard like this. It would melt in your mouth.'

The Mother of Discipline glared at Sister Myrtle. Did the woman ever stop eating? No wonder she was such a size.

'We all have fond memories of our childhood,' observed Sister Grace. 'I don't expect licorice is any better or worse than it used to be.'

'You're wrong there,' mumbled Sister Myrtle. 'We had a corner shop near us that...'

'Can we get on?' cried the Mother of Discipline. 'It's North to bid.'

This was the deal before them:

```
East-West Game          ♠ K 10 3 2
Dealer North            ♡ 7
                        ◇ Q J 6
                        ♣ A K 7 6 4

        ♠ 9 7 6 4                       ♠ Q J 8 5
        ♡ J                N            ♡ Q 6 4 2
        ◇ A K 7 3       W     E         ◇ 8 5 2
        ♣ J 9 8 5          S            ♣ Q 10

                        ♠ A
                        ♡ A K 10 9 8 5 3
                        ◇ 10 9 4
                        ♣ 3 2
```

West	North	East	South
Sister	**Sister**	**Mother**	**Sister**
Grace	**Benedict**	**of Discipline**	**Myrtle**
-	1♣	pass	3♡
pass	3♠	pass	4♡
all pass			

Sister Grace led the king of diamonds and down went the dummy.

'I didn't like your hearts very much,' said Sister Benedict. 'I went Three Spades, hoping you might like them.'

'Your rebid was absurd!' exclaimed the Mother of Discipline. 'Partner holds seven hearts. Of course she doesn't want you to bid Three Spades.'

'It worked out quite well, actually,' declared Sister Myrtle.

Sister Benedict beamed happily. 'I'm so glad I got it right,' she said.

Sister Grace cashed a second round of diamonds, then switched to a spade. Sister Myrtle won with the ace and cashed the ace of trumps, dropping West's jack. West showed out when the trump king was played but there was only one trump to be lost. The contract had been made.

Sister Benedict turned towards the Mother of Discipline. 'Just as well I didn't pass Three Hearts,' she said. 'We'd have missed the game bonus.'

The Mother of Discipline clicked her teeth in agitated fashion. 'Your partner's Three Heart response was as ridiculous as your removal to Three Spades,' she declared. 'One bad bid cancelled out another and you ended in the same contract as everyone else.'

'You're absolutely right,' said Sister Benedict, inspecting the scoresheet. 'Nearly everyone else went down, though.'

'Give me that!' cried the Mother of Discipline, inspecting the scoresheet in disbelief.

'It was the play in trumps, Reverend Mother,' said Sister Grace. 'The percentage play is to cross to dummy and finesse the ten. That picks up three of my five possible singletons.'

The Mother of Discipline raised her eyes to the ceiling. 'Do you see that, Sister Myrtle?' she demanded. 'Not content with misbidding the hand, you managed to misplay it too. Play low to the ten and you win when I hold queen-jack to four.'

'That's not right,' declared Sister Myrtle, reaching for another licorice allsort. 'You would split your honours, wouldn't you?'

'Heaven preserve us!' exclaimed the Mother of Discipline, beckoning for the next board to be brought into position. 'If I split my honours, you would simply win with the ace, cash the king, and knock out the other honour.'

'Yes, I see,' replied Sister Myrtle. 'That would be clever.'

This was the second board of the round:

North-South Game
Dealer East

	♠ 8 6	
	♡ 10 9 8	
	◇ A J 7 2	
	♣ K 10 4 3	
♠ K J 4		♠ Q 10 5 2
♡ J 7 6 2	N W E S	♡ 4
◇ 8 6 3		◇ K 9 5
♣ Q 8 5		♣ J 9 7 6 2
	♠ A 9 7 3	
	♡ A K Q 5 3	
	◇ Q 10 4	
	♣ A	

West	North	East	South
Sister	**Sister**	**Mother**	**Sister**
Grace	**Benedict**	**of Discipline**	**Myrtle**
-	-	pass	1♡
pass	1NT	pass	4♡
all pass			

Sister Grace led ◇6 and down went the dummy. 'Very nice, partner,' said Sister Myrtle. 'Small, please.'

The Mother of Discipline won with the king of diamonds and switched to a spade, taken by South's ace. Sister Myrtle paused to count her tricks. She rarely went to such lengths but it was worth the extra effort against the MD. If you went down in a contract that should have been made, she would rant on for ages.

Now, there were five trump tricks, three diamonds, and three more winners in the black suits. That was a total of eleven. Or, if there happened to be a trump loser, just ten. If she forgot to draw trumps straight away, of course, the defenders might ruff some of her winners. What would the MD say then?

Sister Myrtle drew two rounds of trumps, East showing out on the second round. Only now did a small flaw in the plan occur to her. Suppose she cashed the ace of clubs and turned to the diamond suit. Unless West had started with at least three diamonds, she would ruff the third diamond. She would then return the jack of trumps, pinning dummy's 10 and setting up the seven. With no entry to dummy, there would be three spade tricks to lose. She would be two down!

Sister Myrtle cashed the ace of clubs and, somewhat fearfully, turned to the diamond suit. Luck was with her. Sister Grace followed to the second and third rounds. One spade was thrown on the king of clubs and another on the last diamond. The contract had been made.

'Well played, partner!' exclaimed Sister Benedict. 'Very nicely timed.'

The Mother of Discipline could restrain herself no longer. 'Well played, did you say?' she cried. 'It could scarcely have been played worse.' She turned towards Sister Myrtle. 'Duck the first round of spades. Then you can reach the king of clubs with a spade ruff.'

'That's right,' said Sister Grace. 'You still make eleven tricks if the trumps are breaking.'

Sister Benedict opened the scoresheet. 'Don't worry, partner,' she said. 'Everyone else has done the same. Absolutely flat in 620.'

A disgruntled Mother of Discipline reached for her scorecard. It was absolutely typical of Sister Myrtle's luck to butcher the hand and lose not a single matchpoint by doing so.

'I would offer you a licorice allsort, Reverend Mother,' said Sister Myrtle, 'but they're rather hard. Probably wouldn't suit your teeth.'

The Mother of Discipline made no reply, waiting for the change of round. It was a wonder that Sister Myrtle had any teeth left, she thought, eating sweets all day as she did.

Relief was soon at hand. 'Move for the next round,' called Sister Bernardine.

The Mother of Discipline and Sister Grace departed for the far side of the room and Sister Benedict beamed happily across the table. 'A top and an average against the MD!' she exclaimed.

'It doesn't surprise me,' replied Sister Myrtle. 'She's not the player she used to be.'

Contrary to all form guides, Sister Myrtle and her partner continued to fare well. Neither of them was in the habit of estimating a running score but they could sense that – with a sensible last round – there might be some masterpoints coming their way.

'Ah, good evening, Sister Myrtle,' said the Mother Superior, taking her seat. 'Are you doing well?'

'You're speaking tongue in cheek, I realise, Reverend Mother,' Sister Myrtle replied. 'As it happens, though, we have been doing quite well. We had a complete top against that new novice, Sister Eustace.'

'Did you?' exclaimed the Mother Superior. 'Well played, indeed.'
'Yes, she miscounted her points and they missed a cold game.'
The Mother Superior nodded sympathetically. 'It happens to us all,' she said.
This was the first deal of the round:

```
Game All              ♠ A Q 8 6
Dealer North          ♡ A Q J 9 8 3
                      ◇ —
                      ♣ K Q 8
        ♠ 5                           ♠ J 9 7 3
        ♡ 5 4              N          ♡ K 7 2
        ◇ K Q J 6 4     W   E        ◇ A 10 5
        ♣ 9 7 4 3 2        S          ♣ J 10 6
                      ♠ K 10 4 2
                      ♡ 10 6
                      ◇ 9 8 7 3 2
                      ♣ A 5
```

West	North	East	South
Mother	**Sister**	**Sister**	**Sister**
Superior	**Benedict**	**Thomas**	**Myrtle**
-	1♡	pass	1♠
pass	4NT	pass	5◇
pass	6♣	all pass	

Sister Myrtle arrived in a slam and the king of diamonds was led. Sister Thomas grimaced as the dummy went down. What an absurd Blackwood call! Typical of the luck of these hopeless players that partner's ace should be in clubs, rather than being completely wasted in diamonds.

'That's a nice hand,' said Sister Myrtle. 'Ruff, please.'

The ace and queen of trumps revealed that East held four trumps to the jack. It occurred to Sister Myrtle that it was dangerous to draw trumps before taking the heart finesse. If the heart finesse lost, as most of her finesses seemed to, the defenders would then be able to cash large numbers of diamond tricks.

Sister Myrtle crossed to her hand with the ace of clubs and ran ♡10. Sister Thomas won with the king and returned a second round of diamonds, removing dummy's last trump. These cards remained:

Sr. Benedict
♠ —
♡ A Q J 9 8
◇ —
♣ K Q

M. Superior
♠ —
♡ 5
◇ Q J 6
♣ 9 7 4

	N	
W		E
	S	

Sr. Thomas
♠ J 9
♡ 7 2
◇ 10
♣ J 10

Sr. Myrtle
♠ K 10
♡ 6
◇ 9 8 7
♣ 5

Sister Myrtle now ran dummy's heart suit, throwing diamonds from her hand. Sister Thomas was powerless. If she ruffed at an early stage, declarer would overruff, draw the last trump, and return to dummy with a club. Instead, Sister Thomas tried the effect of discarding her clubs. Declarer, meanwhile, threw her three diamond losers. East had no answer to dummy's last heart. If she discarded a diamond, declarer would throw her club. The lead would be in dummy at Trick 12, with South's ♠K10 poised over East's ♠J9. Sister Thomas eventually decided to ruff the last heart. Declarer overruffed and soon had twelve tricks before her.

'Now I've seen everything,' exclaimed Sister Thomas. 'I'm caught in a trump coup by a declarer who hadn't the faintest...'

'That's enough, Sister!' reprimanded the Mother Superior. 'I will not have other Sisters' play criticised, particularly by those who have not exactly played without error themselves.'

Sister Thomas thought back over the hand. Could she have done anything about it?

'You should duck the first heart,' continued the Mother Superior. 'If declarer repeats the finesse, you play back a club, killing the entry to dummy. Then you can ruff in when the hearts are played.'

Sister Thomas gave a pained shake of the head. How had she missed it? 'Couldn't declarer have prevented that by playing the ace and queen of hearts instead of crossing for a heart finesse?'

'Yes, yes, of course,' replied the Mother Superior. 'No doubt Sister Myrtle, here, was trying for the pairs overtrick.'

Sister Myrtle was delighted that assistance had arrived from such an unexpected quarter. 'Indeed I was, Reverend Mother,' she said.

This was the final hand of the evening:

Game All   ♠ K Q 7
Dealer South   ♡ 10 6 5 3
                    ♢ Q 9 7 4 3
                    ♣ 7

♠ 10 9 8 4 2   ♠ 5 3
♡ J 4   ♡ Q 9 2
♢ J 2   N   ♢ K 10 8 5
♣ J 6 5 3   W   E   ♣ Q 10 9 8
                 S

                    ♠ A J 6
                    ♡ A K 8 7
                    ♢ A 6
                    ♣ A K 4 2

West	North	East	South
Mother	**Sister**	**Sister**	**Sister**
Superior	**Benedict**	**Thomas**	**Myrtle**
-	-	-	2♣
pass	2♢	pass	2NT
pass	3♢	pass	3♡
pass	4♡	pass	4NT
pass	5♣	pass	6♡
all pass			

Sister Myrtle arrived in a small slam and the Mother Superior led ♠10.

'Oh dear, I was hoping for rather more than that,' said Sister Myrtle, spreading the dummy apart with her chubby fingers.

'What on earth can you mean?' snapped Sister Thomas. 'Your partner hardly promised anything with her bidding.'

Sister Myrtle glared resentfully to her right. You could barely open your mouth in this establishment without someone criticising you. Was it against the law to say that she had been hoping for a better dummy?

Sister Myrtle won the spade lead with the jack, cashed the ace of clubs and ruffed a club. She then returned to the ace of spades and ruffed another club. Both defenders followed to the ace and king of trumps and she marked time by cashing the king of clubs. These cards remained:

Sr. Benedict
♠ K
♡ —
◇ Q 9 7 4
♣ —

M. Superior
♠ 9 8 4
♡ —
◇ J 2
♣ —

```
    N
  W   E
    S
```

Sr. Thomas
♠ —
♡ Q
◇ K 10 8 5
♣ —

Sr. Myrtle
♠ 6
♡ 8 7
◇ A 6
♣ —

For want of anything better to do, Sister Myrtle now played a trump. A horrified Sister Thomas won with the queen and had to exit with a diamond. Sister Myrtle sniffed the air. The contract had seemed to have no play at all until now. Wait a moment, though. What if she played low on this diamond trick? If East held the king, which was a 50-50 chance, she would make the contract!

Sister Myrtle played a low diamond from her hand and the Mother Superior could produce only the jack. 'Win with the queen!' said an excited Sister Myrtle. 'I think I've made it now.'

'Beautifully played, partner,' said Sister Benedict.

Sister Thomas closed her eyes. 'May the Lord help me,' she exclaimed. 'It's more than I can tolerate, Reverend Mother. She didn't even cash the third spade before exiting.'

'I could hardly do that,' replied Sister Myrtle. 'That was my last protection in the suit.'

'We needed a diamond lead, Reverend Mother,' declared Sister Thomas. 'That sets up a diamond trick for us and breaks up the endplay.'

The Mother Superior remained as placid as ever. 'I hardly think that jack doubleton in a suit bid by the dummy was a conceivable choice,' she replied. 'We must accept the reverse graciously, as on the previous board.'

The session was over and the players rose to their feet. 'You and Sister Benedict are heading back to your cells, are you?' queried the Mother Superior. 'Sleep well!'

'I don't think I will go straight back on this occasion,' replied Sister Myrtle. 'I usually do but – just this once – I think I'll stay to see what the results are.'

XIII

The Mother of Discipline's Lapse

The Mother of Discipline took the East seat at Table 7, wincing as she flexed the fingers of her right hand. What on earth was the *point* of arthritis? It was painful in the extreme and no-one was very sympathetic about the condition. She moved her copper bangle to a new position, closer to the wrist. What a waste of money that had been, she thought. It had brought no more relief than her prayers on the matter.

'Good evening, Reverend Mother,' said Sister Grace, taking the South seat. 'Sorry to keep you waiting.'

The Mother of Discipline looked in disbelief at the tiny occupant of the North seat. Sister Perpetua, the most useless of the recent intake of novices! 'Is Sister Thomas not good enough for you any more?' she queried.

Sister Grace smiled. 'Sister Thomas is at the local hospital, doing some of her splendid counselling work,' she replied. 'Young Sister Perpetua asked me for a game. I'm sure we'll do well together.'

Not at this table, you won't, thought the Mother of Discipline. This was the first deal:

Love All   ♠ 7
Dealer North   ♡ A K Q 9 5 2
                ◊ 9 8 4
                ♣ J 7 6

♠ 6 5   ♠ A J 10 9 4 3
♡ J 10 8 4   ♡ 7 6 3
◊ Q J 10 7 6   ◊ A K
♣ Q 10   ♣ 5 3

                ♠ K Q 8 2
                ♡ —
                ◊ 5 3 2
                ♣ A K 9 8 4 2

West	North	East	South
Mother Superior	**Sister Perpetua**	**Mother of Discipline**	**Sister Grace**
-	1♡	1♠	2♣
pass	2♡	pass	3NT
all pass			

The Mother Superior led ◊Q against 3NT. The Mother of Discipline cashed two rounds of the suit, then glared at the declarer. Typical of the Sister's luck to find the diamond suit blocked. Expecting declarer to hold the top spades, the Mother of Discipline switched to ♣5. Sister Grace rose with the ace and cashed the king of clubs, dropping West's queen. She then crossed to dummy's jack of clubs, and cashed three top hearts, throwing two spades and a diamond. When a spade was led, the Mother of Discipline had no answer. Whether or not she chose to win this trick, declarer would reach her hand and be able to cash the remaining clubs.

'Ten tricks?' said Sister Grace, facing her remaining cards.

'Ten of the luckiest tricks I have ever witnessed,' declared the Mother of Discipline. 'The diamond suit was blocked *and* the clubs were 2-2. A very fortunate board for you.'

'I'm sure others will fall into the same trap,' observed Sister Grace. 'It was a difficult hand to defend.'

'What on earth do you mean?' said the Mother of Discipline.

'Suppose you play the ace of spades before exiting in clubs, Reverend Mother?' said Sister Grace. 'That stops the endplay. There would be no way back to my hand. Do you see that, Sister Perpetua? It was quite an instructive hand.'

The young novice nodded and began to make a note of the hand on the back of her scorecard.

'Stop that immediately!' cried the Mother of Discipline. 'Do you want all the other competitors to see the hand on your card? If there's any lesson to be drawn from the hand it's that you shouldn't open a one-bid on only 10 points. Do you not play Weak Twos?'

The Mother of Discipline redirected her less than friendly glance to a new target. What had happened to the valuable notion of leading partner's suit? Had the Mother Superior made the obvious spade lead, there would have been no chance at all of an endplay.

A few rounds later, the Mother Superior faced the Convent's most talkative pair, Sister Myrtle and Sister Benedict.

'I could hardly believe it,' said Sister Myrtle, easing her capacious frame into the East chair. 'They had it in every size except 22!'

'Perhaps you could order it, Sister?' her partner suggested.

'I spoke to the manager, I can tell you,' continued Sister Myrtle. 'Do you know what he said? He said there was no demand for size 22 nightdresses nowadays. Have you ever heard such nonsense?'

The Mother of Discipline coughed loudly and indicated, with an arthritic finger, the board that awaited their attention.

North-South Game
Dealer East

	♠ Q J 9 3	
	♡ K 10 6 4	
	◊ Q 2	
	♣ A J 10	
♠ 10 6 4		♠ 7
♡ Q 9 7 2		♡ J 8 5
◊ 9 6 4		◊ A K J 8 5
♣ 7 4 3		♣ K Q 9 2
	♠ A K 8 5 2	
	♡ A 3	
	◊ 10 7 3	
	♣ 8 6 5	

The Mother of Discipline's Lapse

West	North	East	South
Sister	**Mother**	**Sister**	**Mother of**
Benedict	**Superior**	**Myrtle**	**Discipline**
-	-	1◊	1♠
pass	4♠	all pass	

Sister Benedict led ◊9 against the spade game and Sister Myrtle played three rounds of the suit. The Mother of Discipline ruffed the third round in the dummy and paused to consider her continuation. If trumps were 2-2 she could eliminate hearts and have a certain endplay on East.

When the Mother of Discipline played the ace of trumps and a trump to the queen, East showed out on the second round. What next? After East's opening bid the odds were much higher than the normal 24% that she would hold both club honours.

'They had a few Size 22s across the road, at Hedge's,' said Sister Myrtle. 'All their stuff is very flashy, though. Nothing at all suitable for us to wear.'

'Will you be quiet?' exclaimed the Mother of Discipline. 'I'm trying to think.'

'Sorry, Reverend Mother,' replied Sister Myrtle. 'I thought you were taking a rest.'

The Mother of Discipline decided against drawing the last trump. She cashed the two top hearts and ruffed a heart in her hand, removing East's holding in the suit. She then finessed the jack of clubs, losing to the queen. Sister Myrtle had no good card to play. The two safe exit cards, the last heart and the last trump, both lay in her partner's hand.

'Don't spend all night on it,' said Sister Benedict to her partner. 'We don't want to be fined for slow play.'

Sister Myrtle laughed. 'No chance of that on the Reverend Mother's table,' she said. 'Ah well, let's try another diamond.'

South and West both discarded a club and the Mother of Discipline ruffed with dummy's last trump. Since the heart queen was surely with West, she reached her hand at Trick 11 by ruffing a heart. She then faced the king of trumps, West also playing a trump.

'Good gracious!' said the Mother of Discipline mischievously. 'Was there still a trump out?'

'Yes,' exclaimed Sister Benedict. 'I couldn't believe it. I was praying that you would play ace and another club at the end. What a shock it would have been for you if I'd overruffed!'

'It certainly would have been,' said the Mother of Discipline, milking the situation. 'A lucky one for us, partner.'

The Mother Superior maintained a straight face. 'There's no room in the Convent first team for someone who can't even count trumps,' she declared. 'I'm sorry, but I think that Sister Myrtle will have to take your place in the team.'

'You're pulling my leg,' said Sister Myrtle, looking at the Mother Superior with a nervous smile. 'Mind you, I always draw trumps immediately. In fact, I usually draw an extra round if I can afford it, just to make sure.'

This was the second board of the round:

```
Game All              ♠ Q 8 6 2
Dealer South          ♡ A 10 5 4 3
                      ◇ 9
                      ♣ K 8 3
      ♠ 10 9                        ♠ A J 3
      ♡ K J 8 2        N            ♡ Q 9 6
      ◇ A Q 4 3      W   E          ◇ K 8 7 6 2
      ♣ 9 5 2          S            ♣ 7 6
                      ♠ K 7 5 4
                      ♡ 7
                      ◇ J 10 5
                      ♣ A Q J 10 4
```

West	North	East	South
Sister	**Mother**	**Sister**	**Mother of**
Benedict	**Superior**	**Myrtle**	**Discipline**
-	-	-	1♣
pass	1♡	pass	1♠
pass	4♠	all pass	

The ten of trumps was led and down went the dummy. 'A seven-loser hand, as I promised,' said the Mother Superior, arranging her assets into neat columns. 'Those who only count high-card points would undervalue the hand.'

It was not the Mother of Discipline's custom to thank her partner for the dummy, even when it was overflowing with honour cards. When a game raise was backed by a mere nine points, she was tempted to make some adverse comment. With any other partner she would have done. 'Play low,' she said, winning the trick with the king.

Declarer had two losing diamonds to ruff and this would not be possible if West could gain the lead and play another trump, allowing her partner to draw two more rounds. The Mother of Discipline therefore crossed to dummy with the ♥A and led a diamond, hoping that East would go in with a high card. As the cards lay, there was no chance of this. West won the trick with the ◊Q and played another trump. Sister Myrtle drew two more rounds, as declarer had feared, and the contract was one down.

'Excellent trump lead, Sister!' exclaimed Sister Myrtle.

The Mother of Discipline groaned inwardly. It was well known that Sister Benedict nearly always led a trump. If there was anyone else on the planet who was so often 'in doubt' about their opening lead, she had yet to meet them. 'Nine points opposite eleven,' she said. 'Nowhere near enough for game, partner. They'll probably pass the board out at other tables.'

'I would only have raised to Three Spades on your hand, Reverend Mother,' observed Sister Myrtle. 'Sister Benedict and I play a double raise to show a good 9 points up to a bad 12.'

Sister Benedict nodded her agreement. 'Your hand would probably qualify as a good nine rather than a bad nine,' she said.

'The Losing Trick Count usually works all right,' said the Mother Superior. 'You need to find some way to prevent them from drawing three rounds of trumps. What if you rise with the queen of trumps at trick 1? I think you make it then.'

The Mother of Discipline paused to consider this. East would win with the ace of trumps and return a second trump to the king. Yes, but then she could run the club suit. If East refused to ruff, she could throw dummy's diamond loser and proceed with the crossruff. How on earth had she missed such a simple play?

'I considered that line, of course,' said the Mother of Discipline, 'but it costs the overtrick when the opening lead is from 10-9-x. I believe I took the correct line at Pairs.'

'Ah, of course, it was Pairs,' said the Mother Superior, smiling her apologies. 'I knew there must be some reason why you played it that way!'

XIV

Sister Eustace's Compulsory Opening

The Autumn Charity Pairs was about to start and this year a heat was to be held in the novitiate, as well as the main heat in the senior cardroom.

'The movements will be awkward tonight, Reverend Mother,' declared Sister Bernardine. 'We have seven and a half tables in here and four and a half tables in the novitiate.' She scratched her cheek thoughtfully. 'What we could do, I suppose, it to allow one of the stronger novice pairs to play in the senior event.'

A glint came to the Mother of Discipline's eye. 'Rather an ordeal for such young players,' she replied. 'No, if anyone has to make a sacrifice, it is only right that I do it myself. Sister Thomas and I will play in the novitiate heat.'

Sister Bernardine's mouth fell open. 'But some of them scarcely know how to play duplicate,' she said. 'You would outclass them, Reverend Mother. You'd end up with an 80% score.'

'I hardly think the score is of any importance in an event like this,' reprimanded the Mother of Discipline. 'It may have escaped your notice but the purpose of the event is to raise money for a very worthwhile charity.'

There was an apprehensive silence in the novitiate recreation room as the Mother of Discipline made her entrance, with an unhappy Sister Thomas in her wake. The first round saw them facing a pair who had learnt bridge only a month or so before. There was a somewhat unusual auction on the first board:

North-South Game
Dealer East

♠ —
♡ Q J 3
♦ A Q J 9 7 5
♣ K Q J 6

♠ K 9 5
♡ A 9 8 5 2
♦ K 8 2
♣ 9 8

```
  N
W   E
  S
```

♠ J 10 8 7 6 3 2
♡ 10 4
♦ 10
♣ 10 7 4

♠ A Q 4
♡ K 7 6
♦ 6 4 3
♣ A 5 3 2

West	North	East	South
Sister	**Sister**	**Sister**	**Mother of**
Perpetua	**Thomas**	**Helena**	**Discipline**
-	-	3♠	pass
3NT	4♦	pass	6NT
all pass			

When Sister Perpetua heard a 3♠ bid opposite it seemed that 3NT might be on. Give partner seven spades to the ace, plus another card or two, or maybe a diamond lead. Yes, there was every prospect of nine tricks. Sister Thomas entered with 4♦, suggesting a good hand at the score, and the Mother of Discipline decided to take a shot at 6NT.

Unwilling to lead from any of her honours, Sister Perpetua led ♣9. The Mother of Discipline won in the dummy and saw that six diamond tricks would give her the contract. The diamond king was no doubt onside but it might be twice guarded. How could she get to hand twice to take two finesses? The Mother of Discipline smiled to herself. In the senior heat it would be automatic for the defenders to duck the queen and jack of hearts, denying her an entry to the king. The present opponents were certain to grab their ace at the first opportunity. 'Queen of hearts, please,' she said.

East played the four of hearts and West the two. The Mother of Discipline inspected these cards disapprovingly. 'Jack of hearts,' she said.

Once again dummy's card was allowed to win. The Mother of Discipline glared at West. A weak pair like this was bound to finish well below average.

What on earth was the point of them defending this hand so well, spoiling the score of a pair who did have a chance?

If East's ♡10 was anything to go by, it seemed that the hearts were 5-2. Both defenders followed to a second round of clubs. Since West would have led the 10 from ♣1098, it seemed that East must have started with 7-2-1-3 shape and now had the bare ♣10. The club pips were annoyingly disposed. Had ♣5 and ♣6 been exchanged, she could have overtaken dummy's remaining honour, establishing ♣6 as an extra entry.

The Mother of Discipline ground her teeth together. Surely something could be done. She knew how the cards lay, after all. This was the position:

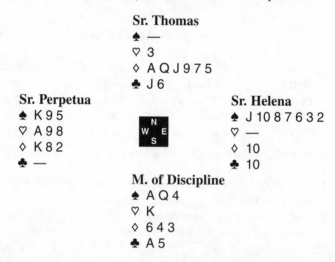

Sr. Thomas
♠ —
♡ 3
◊ A Q J 9 7 5
♣ J 6

Sr. Perpetua
♠ K 9 5
♡ A 9 8
◊ K 8 2
♣ —

Sr. Helena
♠ J 10 8 7 6 3 2
♡ —
◊ 10
♣ 10

M. of Discipline
♠ A Q 4
♡ K
◊ 6 4 3
♣ A 5

An amazing idea suddenly struck the Mother of Discipline. She could throw East in with a club! If East exited with a diamond, this would take one finesse for her and she could cross to the club ace for a second finesse. Nor would East fare any better by exiting in spades. Again two diamond finesses would be possible. 'Play the six of clubs,' instructed the Mother of Discipline.

East won the trick with the 10 and exited with the jack of spades. Nothing was to be gained by risking a finesse and the Mother of Discipline spun the ace of spades onto the table. A diamond finesse succeeded and she returned to the ace of clubs to repeat the finesse. She was then able to claim the contract.

'Brilliant play, Reverend Mother,' exclaimed Sister Thomas. 'Very unusual auction, I must say – going to 6NT over their 3NT.'

Sister Perpetua looked apologetically at her partner. 'I would have taken my ace of hearts if I knew that you had a club trick,' she said. 'I had no idea what to play next if I took the ace, so I thought I'd hold it up until you gave me a discard.'

'I only had three clubs to the 10,' her partner replied. 'I was lucky to make a trick there, really.'

'Unlucky, you mean,' retorted the Mother of Discipline. 'If you had stopped to think about it for a second, you would have unblocked the 10 and seven of clubs. Do you see? I couldn't set up the diamonds then.'

Such divine cardplay would have netted a top in the senior heat, thought the Mother of Discipline. If fact, even in a World Pairs championship it would have been an 80% board. She gave a self-satisfied nod. At this rate there was every prospect of Sister Thomas and herself achieving a top-ten place in the national ranking list.

A round or two later, the Mother of Discipline and Sister Thomas faced the 17-year-old twins, Sister Carla and Sister Celeste. There should be easy pickings here, thought the Mother of Discipline, extracting her cards from the board.

```
Love All              ♠ 8 7 2
Dealer South          ♡ A Q 6
                      ◇ A 8 4 2
                      ♣ K 3 2
        ♠ K Q J 10 9 3            ♠ 6 4
        ♡ 5 4 2            N       ♡ J 10 9 3
        ◇ K 6          W     E     ◇ J 10 9
        ♣ Q 10            S        ♣ J 9 7 4
                      ♠ A 5
                      ♡ K 8 7
                      ◇ Q 7 5 3
                      ♣ A 8 6 5
```

West	North	East	South
Mother of	**Sister**	**Sister**	**Sister**
Discipline	**Celeste**	**Thomas**	**Carla**
-	-	-	1NT
2♠	3NT	all pass	

The Mother of Discipline led ♠K and down went the dummy. 'How do you know your partner has a spade stop?' she demanded. 'Don't you youngsters play Lebensohl?'

'No, we just play Stayman, Reverend Mother,' Sister Celeste replied. 'I didn't think Stayman would apply after your overcall.'

'Lebensohl is what you needed,' persisted the Mother of Discipline. Her king of spades won the first trick and she continued with the queen, annoyed to see the ace appear from declarer. 'Very fortunate,' she declared. 'You might have been completely bare in spades.'

'We usually have a stopper in every suit when we open 1NT,' said Sister Celeste. She gave a small laugh. 'A dog in every kennel, we call it!'

At Trick 3 the young declarer led a low diamond from her hand. 'Eight, please,' she said.

Sister Thomas won with ◊9 but had no spade to return. Her jack of hearts return was won in the dummy. When the ace of diamonds dropped West's king, declarer had nine tricks.

The Mother of Discipline's mouth was open. 'What in Heaven's name was this play in the diamond suit, Sister Celeste?' she demanded. 'It was appallingly against the odds.'

'I'm Sister Carla, actually,' came the reply. 'That's Sister Celeste over there.'

The Mother of Discipline could not care less which twin was which. 'To make game you needed *three* diamond tricks,' she continued. There might be some sense in your play if you needed only two diamond tricks. Finessing the eight was a ludicrous effort on the present hand. You risked going down when East held three diamonds to the king.'

'I was trying to prevent you winning a diamond trick, Reverend Mother.'

The Mother of Discipline struggled to maintain her patience. 'Your play makes the contract only when I hold precisely K-6 of diamonds. Playing ace and another gains when I hold J-6, 10-6 or 9-6. Three times as likely!'

'Yes, I see,' replied the novice, not sounding as if she did. 'Sorry, partner.'

The Mother of Discipline met with mixed fortunes on the next few rounds. With two rounds to go, she estimated her score at two tops above average, some four tops below her original expectations.

'Look out! The MD's heading our way,' exclaimed Sister Eustace. 'She's in a really bad mood today. This morning she gave me five Our Father's, just for walking too fast in the corridor. I wasn't even running, can you believe it?'

'I'd believe anything, as far as the MD's concerned,' replied Sister Alicia. 'She once caught me in the library, reading a letter I'd kept from an old boyfriend...'

'Tell me later,' intervened Sister Eustace. 'Here she is.'

'No welcome for me?' queried the Mother of Discipline, taking her seat.

'Welcome to our table, Reverend Mother,' said the two novices, reciting in harness.

'Let's keep the bidding simple and straightforward,' declared the Mother of Discipline. 'What should it be?'

'Simple and straightforward, Reverend Mother.'

Sister Thomas scored well on a partscore deal. This was the second hand of the round:

```
Game All              ♠ A 10 8 6 4
Dealer North          ♡ K 10 6
                      ◇ J 8 2
                      ♣ 9 4

    ♠ K 3                               ♠ 5
    ♡ J 8 7            N                 ♡ A 9 4 2
    ◇ 10 7 6 5 4    W     E              ◇ Q 9 3
    ♣ Q J 5            S                 ♣ A 10 7 6 2

                      ♠ Q J 9 7 2
                      ♡ Q 5 3
                      ◇ A K
                      ♣ K 8 3
```

West	North	East	South
Sister	**Sister**	**Sister**	**Mother of**
Alicia	**Thomas**	**Eustace**	**Discipline**
-	pass	1♣	1♠
pass	3♠	pass	4♠
all pass			

The queen of clubs was led, taken by the ace, and East returned a second round of the suit. The Mother of Discipline won with the king and paused to consider her prospects. The opening bid surely marked the king of trumps with East. Unless it fell singleton under the ace, everything would depend on the position of the jack of hearts. Wait a moment, surely an elimination would be possible. Yes, of course. The minors could be eliminated and if East started with a doubleton king of trumps she could then be endplayed.

The Mother of Discipline cashed the ace and king of diamonds, ruffed her last club, and cashed the ace of trumps. Both defenders followed but the king refused to show. The Mother of Discipline ruffed dummy's last diamond, then waved a small trump in front of the young East player. 'You're endplayed,' she said. 'A club or a diamond will give a ruff-and-discard, so you'll have to lead a heart.'

Sister Eustace blinked nervously. It was strictly forbidden to contradict the Mother of Discipline in any way, but... how could she be endplayed when she didn't have any trumps left?

'The king of trumps is here, Reverend Mother,' said Sister Alicia.

The Mother of Discipline gave an annoyed click of the teeth. 'We must play on, then,' she said.

West won the second round of trumps and was on lead in this end position:

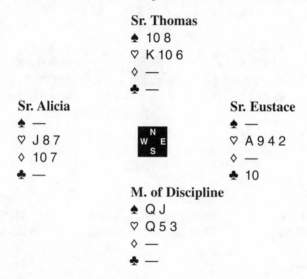

Sr. Thomas
♠ 10 8
♡ K 10 6
♢ —
♣ —

Sr. Alicia
♠ —
♡ J 8 7
♢ 10 7
♣ —

Sr. Eustace
♠ —
♡ A 9 4 2
♢ —
♣ 10

M. of Discipline
♠ Q J
♡ Q 5 3
♢ —
♣ —

Sister Alicia had no idea what cards were still out but she did recall the Mother of Discipline saying that a diamond would give a ruff-and-discard. Somewhat nervously, she placed ♡7 on the table.

The Mother of Discipline sat back in her chair. How many points had East shown up with so far? The ace of clubs and the queen of diamonds, that was all. To make up the thinnest of opening bids, she must surely hold the ace and jack of hearts. 'Play the king, will you?' she said.

Sister Eustace won with the ace and returned ♡2. The Mother of Discipline played low from her hand and could hardly believe it when West produced the jack. She was one down.

The Mother of Discipline reached furiously for the East curtain card. 'You open on a featureless 10-count in a national event?' she cried. 'Did you miscount your points?'

Sister Eustace had turned somewhat pale. 'I had five clubs and four hearts, Reverend Mother,' she said.

'Yes, yes,' replied the Mother of Discipline irritably. 'So what?'

'Well, according to the Rule of 19 I *had* to open,' said Sister Eustace. 'It's a new English Bridge Union ruling. You add your points to the lengths of your two longest suits and if it comes to 19 or more you have to open.'

'St Hilda preserve us!' exclaimed the Mother of Discipline. 'The Rule of 19 gives the *minimum* that you're allowed to open on. Anything less than that has to be reported as a psyche.'

Sister Thomas inspected the scoresheet. 'It's a column of 650s, I'm afraid,' she reported.

The Mother of Discipline reached for her black punishment book. The frivolous opening bid had cost her a full half-top. What would be a suitable punishment, a week of cold showers or a day or two on St Iona's regime? There wasn't much point in cold showers during these summer months; the water was scarcely cold at all. She turned towards Sister Eustace. 'You will take three days on St Iona's regime and write me a letter of apology,' she announced.

Sister Eustace bowed her head. Three days! Even one day would have been a bit harsh, just for a bidding mistake.

'An opening bid like that shows no respect at all for your elders and betters,' declared the Mother of Discipline, wincing as she struggled to her feet. 'I must say I expected a warmer welcome in here, after sacrificing a place in the senior game.'

The final round brought Sister Colleen and Sister Carol to the Mother of Discipline's table. On the first board Sister Carol spent almost ten minutes on a 3NT contract where nine tricks was the only possible outcome. When the Mother of Discipline drew her cards for the final board, most of the other tables had finished play. There was a growing hubbub of conversation. 'Will you be quiet!' she cried. 'This table is still in play.'

A crowd of novices gathered round the table to watch the final board. Sister Theresa had just picked up this hand:

♠ K 9 4
♡ Q 10 4 3
♢ J 8 5
♣ A Q 2

Her partner opened with a 12-14 point 1NT and Sister Thomas passed. Somewhat nervously, Sister Theresa thumbed through her cards. With four hearts she was meant to Stayman for a fit, wasn't she? 'Two Clubs,' she said.

Her partner responded Two Diamonds, denying a major, and Sister Theresa had to consider her next move.

The Mother of Discipline had never liked Sister Theresa. Such shiny, chestnut hair and the young temptress always made sure that little bits of it were left uncovered. 'Come on, come on!' she snapped. 'You're not thinking any more, you're just dithering.'

'Sorry Reverend Mother,' replied Sister Theresa. 'Three Notrumps.'

This was the full deal:

```
Game All           ♠ K 9 4
Dealer South       ♡ Q 10 4 3
                   ◊ J 8 5
                   ♣ A Q 2
   ♠ J 8 3                        ♠ Q 7 5 2
   ♡ 8 5              N           ♡ A 9 6 2
   ◊ A 7 4         W   E         ◊ 10 9 3
   ♣ J 10 9 7 3      S           ♣ K 6
                   ♠ A 10 6
                   ♡ K J 7
                   ◊ K Q 6 2
                   ♣ 8 5 4
```

West	North	East	South
Sister	**Sister**	**Mother of**	**Sister**
Thomas	**Theresa**	**Discipline**	**Katherine**
-	-	-	1NT
pass	2♣	pass	2◊
pass	3NT	all pass	

The jack of clubs was led and Sister Katherine called for dummy's queen. The Mother of Discipline won with the king and returned the suit, declarer winning the third round with dummy's ace. When hearts were played, the Mother of Discipline won with the ace and switched to a diamond. The defenders soon had six tricks before them and the contract was two down.

'I knew I wasn't worth 3NT,' said a disappointed Sister Theresa. 'If I hadn't been hurried, we could have saved a few points by stopping in 2NT.'

'Don't be impertinent,' said the Mother of Discipline. '3NT was a perfectly reasonable contract. Sister Katherine misplayed it, that's all.'

'The standard of cardplay in the novitiate is quite disgraceful,' said Sister Thomas, with a severe twist of the lip. 'A sad reflection on the tuition they receive.'

The Mother of Discipline glared at her partner. 'On the tuition?' she exclaimed. 'I covered this situation only last week. These youngsters never bother to listen, that's the problem.'

'How should I have played it, Reverend Mother?' enquired Sister Katherine.

'She still hasn't seen it!' exclaimed the Mother of Discipline. 'Ace of clubs at Trick 1, of course. Even if you guess to knock out West's ace first, you're still OK. It will go: ten of clubs, queen, king on the second round and I will have no club to return. The contract was cold.'

Sister Thomas, who had suffered from her partner's tongue on numerous occasions, leaned forward. 'If declarer plays the club ace from dummy, you would unblock the king, surely?' she said. 'When she plays a heart you rise with the ace and clear the clubs. It still goes down, then.'

The novices watching at the table hardly dared to move a muscle. Wonderful! They wouldn't have missed this for anything.

The Mother of Discipline's face contorted. 'Do you think I don't realise that?' she cried. 'There's no point muddling the heads of these youngsters. The lesson to be learned is that the ace of clubs should be played, not the queen. You'd never make a good teacher.'

Pardon me for living, thought Sister Thomas, sitting back in her chair. Anyway, wasn't it best to play low from the dummy on the first trick? An unblock from East wouldn't work then.

'I think I know an easy way to help you remember the best play in positions like this,' said the Mother of Discipline, turning her granite-like features towards the young novice.

'That would be very helpful, Reverend Mother,' replied Sister Katherine.

'Copy out the full hand diagram,' continued the Mother of Discipline, 'and draw circles around the cards that should be played at Trick 1.'

'Shall I put a circle round the king in the East hand, Reverend Mother?' queried Sister Katherine.

The Mother of Discipline gave an aggravated wave of the hand. 'Just circle the cards that should be played by West and North,' she replied. 'Twenty copies should be enough. You can bring it to my study tomorrow morning!'

XV

Sister Colleen Cuts In

The Mother of Discipline drummed her fingers on the card table. Where on earth was Sister Thomas? Did she think the three of them had nothing better to do than sit waiting for her all day?

Sister Colleen, an Irish novice who had recently been showing some promise at the game, strolled past the table. 'Do you need fourth, Reverend Mother?' she asked.

The Mother of Discipline viewed the novice with distaste. Forty years ago the rule for novices had been: Do not speak until spoken to. If a novice was ever addressed by the Mother of Discipline, she would quake in her shoes. It was quite different nowadays. Youngsters seemed to have little respect for their elders and betters. 'This game is a bit out of your league, Sister,' the Mother of Discipline replied. 'The stakes are a pound a hundred.'

'That's no problem,' declared Sister Colleen, moving elegantly into the vacant seat. 'The top table in the novitiate is usually a pound game nowadays.'

The Mother of Discipline recoiled. Once upon a time, such a stake would have commanded respect. To refer to someone as a one-pound player would have been a mark of the highest regard. If mere novices were competing for such amounts, perhaps it was time to raise the stake.

Against her better judgement, the Mother of Discipline allowed Sister Colleen to join the game. She regretted this a moment later when she cut the young novice as her partner. The rubber opened with this hand:

Love All
Dealer South

	♠ Q 5	
	♡ 8 5 2	
	◇ A K 10 5	
	♣ A Q 10 3	
♠ A K 8 7 6 4		♠ J 9 2
♡ Q 9 3	N W E S	♡ K 4
◇ J 3		◇ 9 7 6 2
♣ 9 2		♣ 8 7 6 4
	♠ 10 3	
	♡ A J 10 7 6	
	◇ Q 8 4	
	♣ K J 5	

West	North	East	South
Mother of	**Sister**	**Sister**	**Mother**
Discipline	**Grace**	**Colleen**	**Superior**
-	-	-	1♡
1♠	2♣	pass	2♡
pass	4♡	all pass	

The Mother of Discipline led the ace of spades and Sister Colleen contributed the nine. On the king of spades the novice completed her peter, playing the two. Placing her partner with a doubleton, the Mother of Discipline continued with a third round of spades. If partner could overruff dummy's eight, the contract would be one down.

Declarer ruffed the third spade in dummy and Sister Colleen produced the missing jack of spades. The Mother of Discipline emitted a heavy sigh. 'I've never seen anything so absurd,' she declared. 'What's the point of playing for pound stakes when you don't understand the first principles of signalling?'

The Mother Superior discarded a club from her hand, then finessed the jack of trumps, losing to the queen. The Mother of Discipline paused to sniff the air. Declarer had disposed of one club already. If East held the club king it could hardly score a trick, since South would hold the queen of diamonds and four diamond tricks would be enough for the contract. No, the only chance was that Sister Colleen held the king of trumps. In that case a trump promotion would be possible.

The Mother of Discipline led a fourth round of spades and her partner ruffed with the king. Declarer had to overruff and the Mother of Discipline's ♡9 was now promoted into the setting trick.

Sister Colleen looked well pleased with herself. 'You understand my high-low now, Reverend Mother?' she said. 'I could see we had no tricks in the minors, so a trump promotion was the only chance. I had to pretend I had a doubleton, to persuade you to continue the suit.'

The Mother of Discipline directed one of her blackest glances across the table. 'You may have to spoon-feed your partners in the novitiate,' she declared. 'It's not necessary here.'

Maintaining a neutral expression, Sister Colleen wrote down the score.

'I could see from the moment dummy went down that a trump promotion was the only chance,' continued the Mother Discipline. 'Do you think I need you to false-card to tell me you've spotted it too?'

This was the next deal:

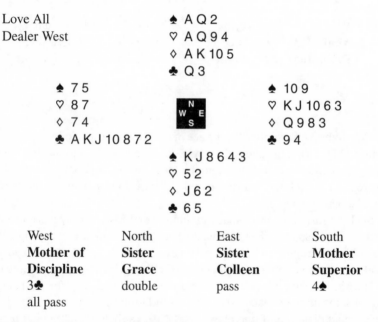

Love All
Dealer West

♠ A Q 2
♡ A Q 9 4
♦ A K 10 5
♣ Q 3

♠ 7 5
♡ 8 7
♦ 7 4
♣ A K J 10 8 7 2

♠ 10 9
♡ K J 10 6 3
♦ Q 9 8 3
♣ 9 4

♠ K J 8 6 4 3
♡ 5 2
♦ J 6 2
♣ 6 5

West	North	East	South
Mother of	**Sister**	**Sister**	**Mother**
Discipline	**Grace**	**Colleen**	**Superior**
3♣	double	pass	4♠
all pass			

With any other partner Sister Grace would have been tempted to look for a slam after the 4♠ response. The Mother Superior usually overbid by a trick, however, and would doubtless need the 21 points in dummy to score just ten tricks.

The Mother of Discipline cashed two club tricks, then switched to ♡8. The Mother Superior had no intention of risking a heart ruff. In any case she knew from the bidding that the king of hearts would be offside. 'Ace, please,' she said.

Trumps were drawn in two rounds, with the ace and jack, leaving this position:

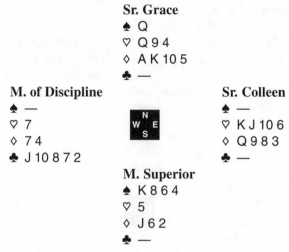

Sr. Grace
♠ Q
♡ Q 9 4
◇ A K 10 5
♣ —

M. of Discipline
♠ —
♡ 7
◇ 7 4
♣ J 10 8 7 2

Sr. Colleen
♠ —
♡ K J 10 6
◇ Q 9 8 3
♣ —

M. Superior
♠ K 8 6 4
♡ 5
◇ J 6 2
♣ —

The Mother Superior led her remaining heart, covering West's seven with dummy's nine. Sister Colleen won with the 10 but had no good return. Hoping that her partner held ◇J, she returned a low diamond. 'They're all there now,' said the Mother Superior, facing her cards.

Sister Colleen gazed across the table. 'Is it better if you switch to a heart at Trick 2, Reverend Mother?' she enquired. 'I would have a safe club exit, then.'

'It makes no difference,' said the Mother Superior. 'I put up the ace, draw trumps in two rounds and play a club. If the Reverend Mother exits with a heart, you're endplayed immediately. If she exits in diamonds, I win with the ace and run the trumps.'

'That's right,' said Sister Grace. 'You're caught in a strip squeeze. Dummy comes down to single ♡Q and ◇K10. If you keep the heart king and queen-one of diamonds, you're thrown in.'

'Obviously,' declared the Mother of Discipline. 'If a heart switch would have beaten it, I would have switched to a heart.'

The rubber had advanced to Game All when the Mother of Discipline picked up this hand:

♠ A K 4
♡ A 10 8 7 2
◇ 6
♣ K J 6 3

'One Diamond,' said Sister Grace, sitting on the Mother of Discipline's left.
'No bid,' said Sister Colleen.
'One Notrump,' said the Mother Superior.

The Mother of Discipline doubled, for take-out, and was surprised to hear a 3NT bid on her left. There was no further bidding and she now had to find a lead. Since there was every prospect of a long diamond suit in dummy, it seemed a good idea to start with the king of spades rather than a fourth-best heart. The Mother of Discipline led the king of spades and down went the dummy:

Game All	♠ 3
Dealer North	♡ K 5
	◊ A K Q 10 8 7 5 2
	♣ 10 4

♠ A K 4
♡ A 10 8 7 2
◊ 6
♣ K J 6 3

	N	
W		E
	S	

West	North	East	South
Mother of	**Sister**	**Sister**	**Mother**
Discipline	**Grace**	**Colleen**	**Superior**
-	1◊	pass	1NT
double	3NT	all pass	

On the king of spades, Sister Colleen signalled with the jack. This was an informative card, indicating possession of the jack-ten but placing declarer with the queen. The Mother of Discipline paused for further calculation. How many points were out? What if declarer held ♠Qxx ♡QJx ◊Jxx ♣Qxxx? Yes, that was plenty for a 1NT response and a club switch would then beat the contract.

At Trick 2 the Mother of Discipline switched to a low club. East produced the queen and the Mother Superior won with the ace. She now waved a finger in the direction of dummy's diamond suit, claiming nine tricks.

The Mother of Discipline scowled at the declarer. 'I did everything possible,' she declared. 'Most people would simply have led a fourth-best heart, giving the contract away when one of the black suits was bare.'

'The spades were bare, actually,' said the Mother Superior.

'I don't believe it!' exclaimed the Mother of Discipline. She glared across the table. 'What was your spade holding?'

'Jack-ten-nine to seven,' replied Sister Colleen. 'Declarer's queen was doubleton.'

'Good gracious, I've never sat opposite such a weak partner,' said the Mother of Discipline. 'If you had seven spades you must have known that the queen was doubleton. You should have signalled with the 10 or the nine, pretending that you held the queen yourself. I'd have continued the suit, then.'

'I would have done that, playing in the novitiate,' replied Sister Colleen. 'On the first hand, though, you said you didn't like partner to direct you with a false card.'

'That was a completely different situation!' cried the Mother of Discipline. 'How in Heaven's name do you think I could place you with seven spades?'

Sister Colleen wisely decided to let the matter drop. It seemed to her, however, that since South's 1NT response had denied four spades, East was marked with either six or seven cards in the suit. Apart from that, if the Mother of Discipline was intending to play her partner for the ace of clubs what could be lost by playing the ace of spades first?

'It's too much to expect a member of the novitiate to even *think* about playing the ten of spades,' continued the Mother of Discipline. 'Four down vulnerable, it would have been. I've never seen such an expensive mistake.'

There was still no sign of Sister Thomas, so the players cut for a second rubber. This time Sister Colleen cut to partner Sister Grace. The novice was soon put to the test.

```
Love All              ♠ A 8 2
Dealer West           ♡ A 2
                      ◇ A 9 5 4
                      ♣ A K 10 7
     ♠ 5                            ♠ 10 6 3
     ♡ Q 10 9 8 7 6 5 3    N        ♡ J 4
     ◇ Q 10 6          W       E    ◇ K J 8 7
     ♣ 2                   S        ♣ Q J 8 4
                      ♠ K Q J 9 7 4
                      ♡ K
                      ◇ 3 2
                      ♣ 9 6 5 3
```

West	North	East	South
Mother of	**Sister**	**Mother**	**Sister**
Discipline	**Grace**	**Superior**	**Colleen**
3♡	double	pass	4♠
pass	6♣	all pass	

The Mother of Discipline deemed a 3♥ pre-empt sufficient on her hand, despite the 8-card suit. Sister Grace doubled for take-out and raised the response of Four Spades to a small slam. The Mother of Discipline led ♣2 and down went the dummy.

Sister Colleen's heart was pounding. A small slam at one-pound stakes! Her earlier statement regarding the stakes in the novitiate game had been somewhat exaggerated. They rarely exceeded 50 pence a 100. The ♣2 lead was surely a singleton but in that case what could be done? The only possibility seemed to be some sort of endplay on East.

Sister Colleen reached for dummy's ace of clubs. She then unblocked the king of hearts and drew two rounds of trumps with the king and ace. West showed out on the second round and the young declarer cashed the ace of hearts, throwing a diamond. Hoping to put East under pressure she then ran a few more rounds of trumps. This end position arose:

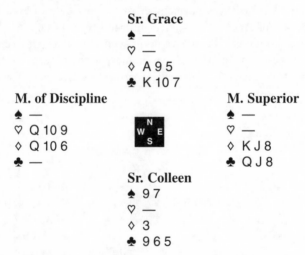

Sr. Grace
♠ —
♥ —
◊ A 9 5
♣ K 10 7

M. of Discipline
♠ —
♥ Q 10 9
◊ Q 10 6
♣ —

M. Superior
♠ —
♥ —
◊ K J 8
♣ Q J 8

Sr. Colleen
♠ 9 7
♥ —
◊ 3
♣ 9 6 5

On the penultimate trump a diamond was thrown from dummy. The Mother Superior now had to throw a card from the East hand. If she released a club, declarer would duck a club, setting up the slam-going trick in that suit. She was therefore forced to throw a diamond.

Sister Colleen now had to hope that East's clubs were accompanied by two diamonds, rather than by one card in each red suit. She crossed to the ace of diamonds and ruffed a diamond, nodding happily when East followed on both rounds. It remained only to play a club to the 10. The Mother Superior had to win with one club honour and lead away from the other. The slam had been made.

'A splendid effort, my child,' declared the Mother Superior. 'Any of us would have been proud to play the hand so well.'

Sister Colleen looked modestly towards the baize. 'Kind of you to say so, Reverend Mother,' she replied. 'There was no other way to play it, really.'

The Mother of Discipline wrote down the score, with stabbing motions of her pen, then turned to glare at the young novice. No doubt she found it amusing to play so hopelessly in partnership with her, then to strike lucky when playing against her. It was no laughing matter, at these stakes.

This was the next deal:

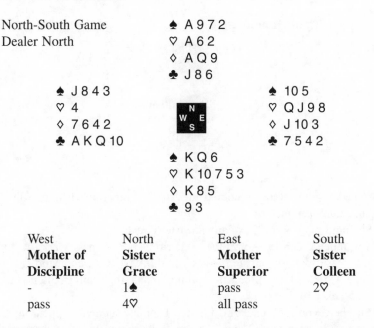

North-South Game	♠ A 9 7 2
Dealer North	♡ A 6 2
	◇ A Q 9
	♣ J 8 6

♠ J 8 4 3		♠ 10 5
♡ 4		♡ Q J 9 8
◇ 7 6 4 2		◇ J 10 3
♣ A K Q 10		♣ 7 5 4 2

	♠ K Q 6
	♡ K 10 7 5 3
	◇ K 8 5
	♣ 9 3

West	North	East	South
Mother of	**Sister**	**Mother**	**Sister**
Discipline	**Grace**	**Superior**	**Colleen**
-	1♠	pass	2♡
pass	4♡	all pass	

The Mother of Discipline led out her three top clubs, declarer ruffing the third round. Sister Colleen crossed to the ace of trumps and played a second round, intending to finesse the 10 as a safety play against a 4-1 break. When the Mother Superior stepped in with the trump queen, the young declarer allowed the card to win. West showed out and the Mother Superior now found the most awkward return – a fourth round of clubs.

Sister Colleen paused to calculate what she should do on this trick. The situation would be hopeless if she reduced her own trumps any further. She would therefore have to ruff in the dummy and rely on a trump coup to pick up East's remaining trumps. What should she discard from her hand?

The defenders held seven diamonds and only six spades. East was more likely to hold three diamonds than three spades, so Sister Colleen threw a spade from her hand. She ruffed with dummy's last trump, then cashed the king and queen of spades. Three rounds of diamonds stood up, leaving the lead in dummy. These cards remained:

Sr. Grace
♠ A 9
♡ —
◇ —
♣ —

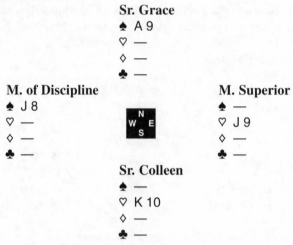

M. of Discipline
♠ J 8
♡ —
◇ —
♣ —

M. Superior
♠ —
♡ J 9
◇ —
♣ —

Sr. Colleen
♠ —
♡ K 10
◇ —
♣ —

A spade from dummy rendered the Mother Superior's trumps valueless. The game had been made.

'Splendid play, Sister!' exclaimed Sister Grace.

'Yes, indeed,' echoed the Mother Superior. 'It does one's heart good to see such fine play from a youngster. Don't you think so, Reverend Mother?'

The Mother of Discipline said nothing, managing a miniscule nod as she reached blackly for her purse.

'Ah, there you are!' exclaimed Sister Thomas, suddenly appearing at the table. 'Sorry to keep you all but I had to assist two of the novices with their bidding homework.'

The Mother of Discipline had never heard such a feeble excuse. Twenty-eight pounds, the session had cost her! Why, it had almost wiped out her winnings for the week.

'It was kind of you to sit in for me,' said Sister Thomas, replacing Sister Colleen at the table. 'The experience didn't prove too costly for you, did it?'

'Very kind of you to be concerned, Sister,' replied Sister Colleen. 'No, I managed to survive, thank you.'

XVI

Sister Thomas's White Lie

The rules and regulations of the Convent were so many and varied that only the most dedicated of incumbents could remember them all.

'Discussion of the previous hand is limited to two sentences!' snapped the Mother of Discipline, reaching for her Punishment Book. 'That really is too bad, Sister Colleen. I pointed it out to you only last week.'

Typical of the MD, thought Sister Colleen. If you ever happened to praise the way she had played a hand, she would allow you a full dozen sentences. Mention how she might have done a bit better and you would be gunned down before you reached the first main verb.

'Since the Our Fathers failed to do their job last week, you will take one day on St Iona's Regime,' continued the Mother of Discipline, making a note to that effect in her book. 'Now, who's to speak first on this one?'

'I believe it's you, Reverend Mother,' said Sister Grace.

This was the board:

East-West Game
Dealer South

```
                    ♠ A J 3
                    ♡ A Q 5
                    ◇ 10 8 3
                    ♣ K 6 5 3
♠ —                              ♠ 9 8 7 4 2
♡ J 9 7 6 2      ┌─────┐         ♡ 10 4
◇ A K J 6 5      │  N  │         ◇ 9 7 2
♣ J 7 2          │W   E│         ♣ Q 9 4
                 │  S  │
                 └─────┘
                    ♠ K Q 10 6 5
                    ♡ K 8 3
                    ◇ Q 4
                    ♣ A 10 8
```

West	North	East	South
Sister	**Sister**	**Sister**	**Mother of**
Carol	**Grace**	**Colleen**	**Discipline**
-	-	-	1♠
pass	2♣	pass	2♠
pass	4♠	all pass	

Sister Carol led ◇A against Four Spades and persisted with two more rounds of the suit. The Mother of Discipline ruffed the third round and played a low trump towards dummy, West showing out.

The Mother of Discipline turned her eagle eyes towards the novice in the West seat, searching for any hint of amusement at the bad trump break. Sister Carol kept her eyes to the baize, not daring to move a muscle.

It seemed to the Mother of Discipline that she would need East to hold three hearts and two clubs. In that case she would be able to run ten tricks, leaving East to trump her partner's club winner at Trick 13. Was there any other chance? Yes, a deceptive play in hearts might help.

The Mother of Discipline drew four rounds of trumps, leaving East with the last trump. She then led a heart to the queen, East playing the four.

'Did the queen win?' croaked the Mother of Discipline, who prided herself on the subtlety of her deceptive plays.

On being assured that it had, she continued with ace and another heart. Many members of the Convent would have been taken in by this virtuoso performance. Sister Colleen was familiar with the Mother of Discipline's style of play, however. Indeed, she had once given a short talk on the matter, in a secret meeting in the novitiate. Apart from that, it was obvious that West would have entered the auction if she held the king of hearts in addition to the diamond suit that she had already shown. Sister Colleen ruffed the third round of hearts, leaving these cards still to be played:

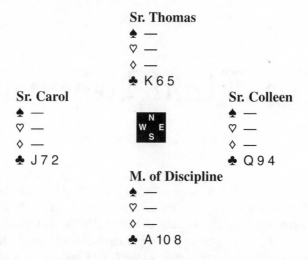

Sr. Thomas
♠ —
♡ —
◊ —
♣ K 6 5

Sr. Carol
♠ —
♡ —
◊ —
♣ J 7 2

Sr. Colleen
♠ —
♡ —
◊ —
♣ Q 9 4

M. of Discipline
♠ —
♡ —
◊ —
♣ A 10 8

A low club from East now would give declarer a chance. By inserting the eight, she could force West's jack and set up a finesse of the 10. Sister Colleen made no such mistake. She exited with the ♣Q and the contact had to go one down.

'Someone Up There is in a bad mood today,' declared the Mother of Discipline. 'I can't think what I've done to deserve a trump break like that.'

'Was there any way of making the contract?' enquired Sister Colleen, making full use of the first sentence that she was allowed.

The Mother of Discipline's eyes bulged and Sister Thomas leaned forward, coming to her rescue. 'Of course not, child,' she reprimanded. 'If there was, the Reverend Mother would have found it.'

Sister Thomas made a mental note to confess this falsehood at Father O'Regan's next visit. The contract could easily have been made by discarding a club at Trick 3 instead of ruffing. A fourth round of diamonds could then have been ruffed with dummy's ♠3. It would do East no good to overruff because declarer would overruff in turn, proceeding to draw trumps.

'I may be eighty-two years old,' the Mother of Discipline informed Sister Colleen, 'but when it comes to playing the cards I don't think anyone in the Convent would claim to be as good.'

'No indeed, Reverend Mother,' replied Sister Colleen, smiling sweetly at her ancient adversary.

They wouldn't dare.

XVII

The Final Rehearsal

It was the evening before a second-round Gold Cup match and the Mother of Discipline was keen that the two pairs in the team should put up a sound performance in the Friday pairs. 'Don't waste the occasion by indulging in your usual rabbit-killing tactics,' she instructed Sister Thomas. 'Bid soundly for a change. We'll need to tomorrow in the Gold Cup.'

'Every pair plays a different game,' replied Sister Thomas.

'What's that supposed to mean?' asked the Mother of Discipline.

'The Mother Superior and I like to apply a little pressure,' continued Sister Thomas. 'To bid soundly, as you put it, can make life easy for the opponents.'

'I see,' replied the Mother of Discipline, who was unaccustomed to having her advice ignored. 'And I suppose going for 800 in some two-level overcall on ace-jack to five makes life difficult for them.'

The Mother of Discipline and Sister Grace had made a sound start in the pairs when, on Round 6, Sister Myrtle and Sister Benedict arrived at their table. The Mother of Discipline watched disapprovingly as Sister Myrtle wedged herself into the East seat. Good gracious, what a size she was! Did the list of Deadly Sins on her cell door not include Gluttony? She must spend half the day eating.

'Would you like a Rowntree's fruit gum, Reverend Mother?' asked Sister Myrtle, proffering a freshly opened tube.

The Mother of Discipline shook her head. She didn't approve of eating between meals. In any case, there was a yellow fruit gum on top, not one of her favourites.

The other two players accepted the offer, then turned their attention to this board:

Game All   ♠ 5 3 2
Dealer South   ♥ 10 5 4
                  ◊ K Q J 8
                  ♣ A Q 10

```
♠ 10 7                          ♠ 9 4
♥ K 9 3          N              ♥ Q 8 7
◊ 10 7 6 4 3 2  W   E           ◊ 9 5
♣ 3 2               S           ♣ K J 8 7 6 4
```

                  ♠ A K Q J 8 6
                  ♥ A J 6 2
                  ◊ A
                  ♣ 9 5

West	North	East	South
Sister	**Sister**	**Sister**	**Mother of**
Benedict	**Grace**	**Myrtle**	**Discipline**
-	-	-	2♠
pass	3♠	pass	4◊
pass	5♣	double	6♠
all pass			

'Is it my lead?' asked Sister Benedict.

'Yes,' replied Sister Myrtle. 'The Reverend Mother opened Two Spades, then went to Six Spades over my lead-directing double in clubs.'

The Mother of Discipline shuddered at this lack of ethics. Had one of the novices made a similar comment, she would have been reaching for her punishment book. Sister Benedict led ♣3 and down went the dummy. The Mother of Discipline viewed the entry situation with no great enthusiasm. Three trumps to the five? Had there been three trumps to the 10, she could have reached the blocked diamond honours in dummy.

Sister Myrtle, meanwhile, was eyeing her partner's ♣3. If that wasn't a singleton, she didn't know what was! How splendid it would be if the Reverend Mother were to take a finesse and suffer a ruff on the return. Mind you, she would hardly make such a mistake after the lead-directing double.

The Mother of Discipline waved a resigned finger in the direction of dummy's club suit. Play the ten,' she instructed.

Sister Myrtle could not believe her luck. She won with the jack and, almost before declarer had followed to the trick, fired back another club. She stared in disbelief when West followed with the two. Three-two doubleton? What was the chance of being dealt that holding? It must be about 100-to-1 against. In need of consolation, Sister Myrtle reached for her tube of fruit gums. Yes, there was a blackcurrant one on top! Why they included those yellow, lemon-flavoured ones was a mystery. She had never met anyone who liked them.

The Mother of Discipline was by no means overjoyed at this club return. Although Sister Myrtle had little idea what she was doing, she had in fact killed the entry to the blocked diamond suit. What could be done? If the ace of clubs were to stand up, she could discard the ace of diamonds. Provided the diamonds broke no worse than 5-3, she would then be able to discard her three losing hearts. Any sort of minus score on the deal was hardly likely to trouble the scorer, so the risk would have to be taken. 'Ace of clubs,' said the Mother of Discipline.

The diamond ace was discarded but West struck with a trump. The Mother of Discipline, feeling as if she were in the middle of a strange nightmare, won the trump return and drew the outstanding trump. She then led a heart to the 10, a play that would restrict the damage to two down if the outstanding heart honours lay in the same hand. No, East won with the queen and returned ♡7, covered by the jack and king. The slam was three down.

Sister Grace smiled sympathetically at her partner. 'That was bad luck,' she observed.

'It's easily done, though,' said Sister Myrtle, who was struggling with the wrapper on a new pack of fruit gums. 'If truth be told, I've made the same mistake myself, many a time.'

'Mistake, what mistake?' exclaimed the Mother of Discipline.

Sister Myrtle placed a green fruit gum in her mouth, noting that the next one in the tube was yellow. 'Well, it was tempting to go for the overtrick by finessing the queen of clubs,' she mumbled, 'but, of course, if you rise with the ace and draw trumps you don't run into that ruff. Are you sure you wouldn't like a fruit gum, Reverend Mother?'

'What nonsense you talk!' cried the Mother of Discipline. 'The diamond suit was blocked. Didn't you notice?'

Sister Grace inspected the scoresheet. 'Six notrumps by North is the best spot,' she said. 'There are three 1440s on the sheet.'

'I thought as much,' said the Mother of Discipline. 'You were the one looking at A-Q-10 of clubs, not me.'

'True,' replied Sister Grace. 'I was also the one looking at three hearts to the 10.'

A round or two later, two of the less experienced novices arrived at the Mother of Discipline's table. Somewhat nervously Sister Ambrosine and Sister Perpetua took their seats.

'Look at your hair, child!' exclaimed the Mother of Discipline.

'Is there something wrong with it, Reverend Mother?' asked Sister Ambrosine.

'It's showing under your wimple, at the front and the side!' continued the Mother of Discipline. 'Do you enjoy parading your shiny hair in front of those whose hair has gone grey or white?'

'No, indeed, Reverend Mother,' declared Sister Ambrosine. 'I checked it carefully before the session. It must have worked its way loose.'

Mother of Discipline's right hand reached automatically towards her Punishment Book. 'I'll be lenient on this occasion,' she declared. 'Don't make me regret it, with any similar poor grooming in the future. That will be three written copies of the Act of Contrition.'

The players drew their cards for this deal:

Game All
Dealer North

	♠ K Q 10 7 6 2	
	♡ K 6 5 2	
	◇ K 4	
	♣ 8	
♠ A 9 4		♠ J 8 5 3
♡ Q 10 9 7		♡ —
◇ Q 6 3		◇ 10 9 7 5 2
♣ K Q 7		♣ J 9 4 3
	♠ —	
	♡ A J 8 4 3	
	◇ A J 8	
	♣ A 10 6 5 2	

West	North	East	South
Sister	**Sister**	**Sister**	**Mother of**
Ambrosine	**Grace**	**Perpetua**	**Discipline**
-	1♠	pass	2♡
pass	4♡	pass	6♡
double	all pass		

Sister Ambrosine was in a dilemma when the Mother of Discipline bid Six Hearts in front of her. If she doubled, and picked up 500 or so, the MD was hardly likely to be lenient in any future close decision on punishments. If she failed to double, however, it would be all too obvious that she was trying to curry favour. Surely, with four defensive tricks in her hand, she was obliged to double.

The king of clubs was led and the Mother of Discipline won with the ace. It would be hard work to set up either of the black suits and she decided to try her luck with a crossruff. She ruffed a club and called for dummy's king of spades. When East followed impassively with a low card, the Mother of Discipline ruffed in her hand. After cashing two top diamonds, she took two further ruffs in each hand. The lead was with declarer in this end position:

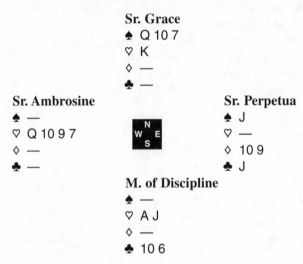

Sr. Grace
♠ Q 10 7
♡ K
◇ —
♣ —

Sr. Ambrosine
♠ —
♡ Q 10 9 7
◇ —
♣ —

Sr. Perpetua
♠ J
♡ —
◇ 10 9
♣ J

M. of Discipline
♠ —
♡ A J
◇ —
♣ 10 6

Peering triumphantly at young Sister Ambrosine, the Mother of Discipline ruffed a club with dummy's king. 'Spade queen,' she said.

Declarer threw the last club from her hand and Sister Ambrosine ruffed in the West seat. A trump into declarer's tenace then surrendered the slam.

'Foolish double, girl!' exclaimed the Mother of Discipline. 'You gave away the lie of the cards. A good declarer couldn't go down after your double.'

A smiling Sister Grace leaned forward. 'You played it well, Reverend Mother,' she said. 'Doesn't a trump lead beat it, though?'

The Mother of Discipline was somewhat exhausted by her efforts on the deal and could not be bothered with any further analysis. 'You obscure the main point of the hand, Sister,' she replied. 'The double was a foolish one, particularly against a strong declarer.'

Towards the end of the evening the Mother Superior and Sister Thomas arrived. 'I see you've been picking up some good scores tonight,' observed the Mother Superior, taking her seat.

The Mother of Discipline looked up uncertainly. 'Which ones were you thinking of?' she asked.

'Wasn't it you who took plus 300 when Sister Myrtle and Sister Benedict ended in Six Spades?' said the Mother Superior. 'Absurd not to play in notrumps, of course.'

'Er... no, that must have been someone else,' replied the Mother of Discipline. 'That pair didn't bid any slams against us.'

This was the first board of the round:

```
North-South Game        ♠ A Q 7 2
Dealer North            ♡ A J
                        ◊ 9 7 3
                        ♣ A Q 7 4
        ♠ 10 9                          ♠ K
        ♡ K 7 6 2          N            ♡ Q 10 9 3
        ◊ A Q 8 4 2     W     E         ◊ J 10 6
        ♣ 10 5             S            ♣ K 9 8 3 2
                        ♠ J 8 6 5 4 3
                        ♡ 8 5 4
                        ◊ K 5
                        ♣ J 6
```

West	North	East	South
Sister	**Sister**	**Mother of**	**Mother**
Grace	**Thomas**	**Discipline**	**Superior**
-	1♣	pass	1♠
pass	4♠	all pass	

The auction suggested a red-suit lead but Sister Grace was unimpressed by her holdings in that department. She led the ten of trumps and down went the dummy.

The Mother of Discipline winced at the sight of dummy's trump holding. It was typical of Sister Grace to lead a trump at such a moment!

'Ace, please,' said the Mother Superior.

With an annoyed click of the teeth the Mother of Discipline displayed the trump king. She then turned towards Sister Thomas. 'How on earth can you raise to four on a flat six-loser hand like that?' she demanded. 'Give partner four small trumps and a couple of kings and you would probably go down in Three Spades.'

'I always bid up when I hold three aces,' Sister Thomas replied.

The Mother Superior drew a second round of trumps with the queen, then paused to consider her continuation. After the slice of good fortune in the trump suit the contract would be at risk only when both minor-suit cards were offside. What could be done in that case? Ah yes, of course. 'Small club, please.'

The Mother of Discipline looked at this card uncertainly. It was possible that declarer held ♣10-x and was tempting her to play the king prematurely. She might make the same play with a singleton ♣J too. It seemed to the Mother of Discipline that the situation did not lend itself to precise analysis. She rose with the king of clubs and switched to the jack of diamonds, West scoring two tricks in the suit. These were the last tricks to come the defenders' way. Dummy's club suit provided two discards for declarer's heart losers and the game had been made.

'It's no better if you duck in clubs,' said the Mother Superior. 'I can give up a heart and ruff a heart.'

'Obviously,' grunted the Mother of Discipline. She turned to her right, directing a further disapproving glance in Sister Thomas's direction. 'I trust you're not going to bid so wildly in the Gold Cup match tomorrow.'

'You don't think plus 620 would be a useful board at IMPs?' retorted Sister Thomas.

'On a normal heart lead there would be four certain losers,' continued the Mother of Discipline. 'You'd lose a trick to the king of trumps, as well. Two Spades was the limit of the hand.'

The players drew their cards for the second board of the round.

Love All	♠ J 6 3	
Dealer East	♡ A 5	
	◇ A Q 5 4	
	♣ A 9 4 2	

♠ A K Q 7		♠ 9 8 4
♡ 7 2		♡ J 10 6
◇ K 10 9 6 3		◇ J 8 2
♣ J 6		♣ 10 8 7 3

```
        N
     W     E
        S
```

	♠ 10 5 2	
	♡ K Q 9 8 4 3	
	◇ 7	
	♣ K Q 5	

West	North	East	South
Sister	**Sister**	**Mother of**	**Mother**
Grace	**Thomas**	**Discipline**	**Superior**
-	-	pass	1♥
double	redouble	pass	2♥
pass	4♥	all pass	

Showing support for her partner's chosen tactics, the Mother Superior opened light in the first seat. Her immediate 2♥ rebid over the redouble showed this type of hand and Sister Thomas raised to the heart game, expecting her partner to hold six hearts.

Sister Grace opened the defence by cashing three rounds of spades. It seemed almost inconceivable, with such a strong dummy, that the defenders could score a fourth trick. Uncertain of exactly what might happen, Sister Grace tried the effect of a fourth round of spades. A club was thrown from dummy and the Mother of Discipline ruffed with the jack, overruffed by declarer's queen.

The Mother Superior now had to divine the lie of the remaining trumps. West's take-out double suggested shortage in hearts. She could scarcely hold a small singleton, since East would not have ruffed from J-10-x-x, a sure trump trick. If West held a small doubleton trump, she was unlikely to have seen any future in a fourth round of spades. No, the most likely situation was surely that West held three trumps to the ten, with a hand such as:

    ♠ A K Q 7
    ♥ 10 7 2
    ♦ K J 10 3
    ♣ J 6

The Mother Superior advanced the nine of hearts from her hand, West playing low. 'Small, please,' she said.

The Mother of Discipline paused dramatically, then won with the trump ten. The game was one down.

'Clever defence,' said the Mother Superior, with a respectful nod in Sister Grace's direction.

'Yes, I thought the jack would fool you,' declared the Mother of Discipline. 'Contrary to what some might say, there's life in the old fox yet.'

The Mother Superior managed to keep a straight face. 'If our Gold Cup opponents had seen that defence of yours, Reverend Mother, they would be worried men.'

The Mother of Discipline sat back in her chair, nodding happily. 'They wouldn't sleep easily in their beds tonight, you're right,' she replied.

XVIII

Professor Barclay's Calculations

In the second round of the Gold Cup the St Hilda's team had been drawn away to a team from Oxford University.

'No idea what sort of opposition to expect,' said the Mother Superior, as she steered her small Renault out of the convent gates. 'Probably a bunch of long-haired students who think they know everything about the game.'

Sister Grace leaned forward. 'I don't believe students have long hair nowadays,' she said. 'Most of them look surprisingly presentable, in fact.'

'Just as well it wasn't a home match,' said the Mother of Discipline. 'You can just imagine our novices peering out of the window, gawking at the young men as they arrived.'

'I don't believe it's sinful to take a mild pleasure in the human form,' declared the Mother Superior.

'Neither do I,' said the white-haired Sister Grace. She gave Sister Thomas a playful nudge. 'I'm rather looking forward to the match, in fact.'

Sister Thomas moved away from her colleague, wedging herself against the car door. 'I realise that you're joking,' she said. 'I don't think it's very suitable conversation material anyway.'

The St Hilda's team was soon being welcomed into Balliol College. The Mother Superior had a very mixed record against student teams and was delighted to find that the opposing team consisted of four elderly academics. The first set saw her facing the opposing captain, Professor Barclay. This was an early board:

Game All
Dealer North

```
              ♠ J 3
              ♡ J 5 4
              ◇ K J 8 5
              ♣ A K 9 6
♠ K 9 7 6 2                      ♠ A 8 4
♡ Q 7 2          N              ♡ K 10 8 6 3
◇ 6          W       E          ◇ Q 9 3
♣ Q 10 8 3       S              ♣ 7 4
              ♠ Q 10 5
              ♡ A 9
              ◇ A 10 7 4 2
              ♣ J 5 2
```

West	North	East	South
Sister	**Dr.**	**Mother**	**Professor**
Thomas	**Milner**	**Superior**	**Barclay**
-	1◇	pass	2NT
pass	3NT	all pass	

'Baron 2NT, was it?' enquired Sister Grace, who was on lead.

'No, no,' replied Dr. Milner a tall grey-faced man. 'We don't play any of the ultra-modern gadgets.'

Sister Thomas raised a bushy eyebrow. Ultra-modern? The Baron 2NT response had been conceived in the 1940s, surely. She led ♣6 and the Mother Superior won with the ace. When ♣8 was returned, Professor Barclay tempted a cover by playing the queen from his hand. Since her partner would not have returned the eight from an original A-10-8-4, Sister Thomas was not tempted to capture the trick. She allowed the queen to hold, maintaining a link with her partner.

Since the defenders were poised to score three more spade tricks, everything now depended on the view that declarer took of the diamond suit. Professor Barclay gave the matter little thought. He crossed to the king of diamonds and played a low diamond to the 10. A few moments later he was entering a +600 in his scorecard.

Sister Thomas looked blankly at the Professor. 'That was an inspired view in diamonds,' she said.

The Professor gave a small laugh. 'I always play with the odds,' he declared. 'You would hardly expect otherwise from a Regis Professor of Applied Statistics.'

'I don't follow you,' said Sister Thomas. 'Why was it with the odds to finesse my partner for the queen?'

The Professor smiled patiently. Was it possible for a mere woman to understand anything based on cold logic? He would go through the motions of explaining, to be polite, but there was little point in it. 'We call it the Law of Vacant Spaces in the trade,' he replied. 'You had five spades to your partner's three, so your partner had ten vacant spaces to your eight that could be used to accommodate diamonds. The odds were that she would hold longer diamonds.'

'But spades wasn't a random suit,' persisted Sister Thomas. 'It was the suit that I chose to lead against 3NT. Suppose you had been playing a weak notrump and your partner had opened 1NT, raised to 3NT. The Mother Superior would have led a heart. When your partner found out that hearts were 5-3 he would, according to your theory, deduce that I held the queen of diamonds. In other words, you're claiming that the defender not on lead is always a favourite to hold a missing queen!'

Professor Milner could not, for the moment, see the flaw in this argument. It was faulty in some way, obviously. 'A fallacious argument, I'm afraid,' he declared. 'The Law of Vacant Spaces has been a heavy money-earner for me over the years, I can assure you.'

'It's true,' said his grey-faced partner. 'And we're talking about a high standard of game, in the Balliol common room.'

Meanwhile, at the other table, the Mother of Discipline and Sister Grace faced a couple of distinctly long-in-the-tooth Classics lecturers. They were about to play this board:

Love All	♠ K J 5
Dealer North	♡ A J 4 2
	◇ Q 8 3
	♣ Q 8 5

♠ 4		♠ 9 3
♡ 9 7 6	N W E S	♡ K Q 10
◇ 10 6 5 2		◇ A J 9 4
♣ J 10 9 6 2		♣ A K 7 3

| ♠ A Q 10 8 7 6 2 |
| ♡ 8 5 3 |
| ◇ K 7 |
| ♣ 4 |

West	North	East	South
Dr.	**Sister**	**Dr.**	**Mother of**
Parkes	**Grace**	**Coulter**	**Discipline**
-	1NT	double	4♠
all pass			

The bald-headed Dr. Parkes started with the jack of clubs.

'Normal leads?' queried the Mother of Discipline.

'Prima inter pares, yes', replied the skeletal Dr. Coulter, sitting East. 'We lead the top honour from a sequence.'

Dr. Parkes leaned forward, with the air of someone about to unleash a witticism. 'I dare say you ladies expected two Classics dons to play Roman leads,' he said. 'Hah, hah, *secunda inter pares*, as it were. We did try them for a while, actually. Found them too confusing.'

The 82-year-old Mother of Discipline surveyed her opponent somewhat unsympathetically. Why on earth was the university still paying a salary to such an old fool? Was the concept of retirement unknown in the City of Spires? She turned her gaze towards the dummy. She could not afford to waste the club queen; it might be needed as a throw-in card later. She would have to play low, hoping that West was dim enough to play another club. 'Small, please,' she said.

The Mother of Discipline ruffed the club continuation, crossed to the king of trumps, and led a diamond towards her hand. East could not afford to go in with the ace and declarer's king won the trick. A trump to dummy's jack left these cards still to be played:

Sr. Grace
♠ 5
♡ A J 4 2
♦ Q 8
♣ Q

Dr. Parkes
♠ —
♡ 9 7 6
♦ 10 5 2
♣ 9 6

Dr. Coulter
♠ —
♡ K Q 10
♦ A J 9
♣ A K

M. of Discipline
♠ A Q 10 7
♡ 8 5 3
♦ 7
♣ —

'Play the queen of clubs,' said the Mother of Discipline.

The king appeared from East and declarer discarded her last diamond. Dr. Coulter marked time by leading the king of hearts but this card was allowed to win. He then gave a sigh, realising that he had reached the end of the line. He spun a resigned ace of diamonds on to the table and the Mother of Discipline ruffed. The remaining heart loser was discarded on the queen of diamonds and ten tricks resulted.

'Yes, I could see that declarer might manage that sort of ending,' declared the East player. 'We needed a heart switch at trick two, Eric. Didn't you see my low club?'

'Of course,' replied his partner. 'I gave serious consideration to a heart switch but it seemed too dangerous.'

'Audere est facere,' reprimanded Dr. Coulter.

'Solum ineptus gradum in aquam nigram facit,' countered his colleague.

Sister Grace smiled. 'Catullus?' she queried.

'Yes, indeed,' replied a surprised Dr. Parkes. 'I see we've encountered a rare pocket of civilisation here.'

The boards ticked by with neither side being able to create any sizeable lead. The Mother Superior had the feeling that the Convent team was greatly superior in all aspects of the game. For some strange reason, though, this superiority was taking a long time to assert itself on the score-sheet. With just one set to play, the Oxford team led by 9 IMPs.

The final set once again placed the two captains in opposition.

```
Game All              ♠ J 9 3
Dealer East           ♡ 10 4
                      ◇ A Q 5
                      ♣ A 8 6 4 3
      ♠ Q 10 7 2                      ♠ K 8 5
      ♡ 8 7 3          N              ♡ K Q J 9 6 5
      ◇ 9 7 6 4      W   E            ◇ J 10 3
      ♣ K 2            S              ♣ J
                      ♠ A 6 4
                      ♡ A 2
                      ◇ K 8 2
                      ♣ Q 10 9 7 5
```

West	North	East	South
Sister	**Dr.**	**Mother**	**Professor**
Thomas	**Milner**	**Superior**	**Barclay**
-	-	1♡	2♣
pass	2♡	pass	3♣
pass	5♣	all pass	

The academics overbid to a poor game in clubs and Sister Thomas led ♡7. 'I hope I haven't said too much on this,' said Dr. Milner, laying out his somewhat modest dummy.

The Professor won with the ace and paused to consider how he might conjure eleven tricks. Springing to life, he led the queen of clubs from hand, running the card when it was not covered. The Mother Superior followed with the jack on this trick and could not believe it when her partner's king appeared on the next round of trumps. What a phenomenal view to take! Particularly after she had opened the bidding.

Declarer cashed three rounds of diamonds to leave this end position:

Dr. Milner
♠ J 9 3
♡ 10
◇ —
♣ 8 6 4

Sr. Thomas
♠ Q 10 7 2
♡ 8 3
◇ 9
♣ —

M. Superior
♠ K 8 5
♡ K Q 9 6
◇ —
♣ —

Prof. Barclay
♠ A 6 4
♡ 2
◇ —
♣ 10 9 7

The Mother Superior had to win the heart exit in the East seat. Her partner's seven, followed by the eight, had indicated a three-card holding. That left declarer with no more hearts, so there was no choice but to play a spade now. Which spade should she play?

The only case of interest was when West held the queen and 10, concluded the Mother Superior. It was obvious what would happen on a low spade exit. It would run to West's queen and declarer couldn't possibly go wrong on the return, the opening bid marking East with the king. However, what would happen if she exited now with the *king* of spades? Surely declarer would place her with the king-queen and duck the trick, hoping to force a lead from the remaining honour? Glowing slightly from her mental exertions, the Mother Superior placed the king of spades on to the table.

Professor Barclay slapped his ace on the trick and returned a spade. The party was over. Sister Thomas rose with the queen and declarer had the remainder.

The Professor turned in friendly fashion towards the Mother Superior. 'I couldn't go wrong there, fortunately,' he said. 'Your partner had the queen and the ten.'

The Mother Superior suddenly felt drained of all strength. 'Did you not think I might hold the king and queen of spades?' she enquired.

'I thought it was a near certainty after the opening bid,' replied the Professor. 'I'd still be all right if your partner held the 10, though. Dummy's nine would force your queen.'

What have I done to deserve this, thought the Mother Superior. It hadn't even occurred to the old codger to play low on the ♠K switch.

'I hardly dare ask how you took such a good view in the trump suit,' said the Mother Superior. 'Isn't it better odds to play to drop the king?'

'Ah, no, you're definitely wrong there,' declared the Professor. 'That's an old wives' tales, if you'll pardon the expression.'

'What is?' persisted the Mother Superior.

'You know, the business about the king of clubs always being a singleton. In fact, we've been keeping meticulous records of singleton club honours for over three years now. A colleague of mine in the Computer Sciences faculty has promised to analyse the data.'

The Professor reached for his pocket diary and made an entry in one of the back pages. 'Yes, so far the jack of clubs has been singleton 172 times, including just now, and the king of clubs was singleton only 158 times.' He looked triumphantly at the Mother Superior. 'You see?' he exclaimed. 'I knew I was right.'

The other St Hilda's pair had produced no miracles at their table and the Oxford team had won the match by 13 IMPs.

'It's a more mathematical game than you imagine,' declared the Professor, escorting the visiting team to the Balliol front gate. 'Still, playing by instinct as you were, I must congratulate you. You gave us a very hard fight!'

XIX

𝕿𝖍𝖊 𝕳𝖆𝖓𝖉𝖎𝖈𝖆𝖕 𝕻𝖆𝖎𝖗𝖘

Once a year the Convent held a Handicap Pairs competition. The partnerships were determined from an overall ranking list of the senior players, the novices being excluded. The highest ranking player would partner the lowest ranking, the second highest would partner the second lowest, and so on.

The Mother of Discipline made it her task to adjust the ranking list every year, taking account of everyone's latest form. She had just posted onto the notice board her carefully considered rankings for the current season. They were headed by:

1.	*Mother of Discipline*	*+4.2 tops*
2.	*Sister Grace*	*+3.9 tops*
3.	*Mother Superior*	*+3.7 tops*

Bringing up the rear were:

22.	*Sister Benedict*	*–3.7 tops*
23.	*Sister Myrtle*	*–4.9 tops*
24.	*Sister Consolata*	*–5.0 tops*

It was almost a contradiction in terms to place anyone below Sister Myrtle and in fact the Welsh nun, Sister Consolata was not too bad a player. It was only because she played so infrequently that the Mother of Discipline could justify placing her in 24th place, where – as it happened – she would be partnering the player ranked in top place.

The Mother of Discipline had won the event with Sister Consolata the previous year and had high hopes of repeating the success. She was about to head for the cardroom when there was a knock on the door.

'Only me,' said Sister Myrtle, squeezing her way into the room. 'I thought we'd better discuss our system before play starts.'

The Mother of Discipline's mouth fell open. 'What on earth do you mean?' she demanded. 'You're partnering Sister Grace, aren't you?'

'No, Sister Consolata is having to nurse Sister Euphemia in the infirmary,' came the reply. 'Very unfortunate for me, of course, because it drops me to the bottom of the list.'

The Mother of Discipline looked as if she had been cornered by a mad gunman. 'If we're one short, there must be an odd number of players,' she said. 'You'll have to drop out and I can partner Sister Benedict.'

'No need for that,' replied Sister Myrtle. 'Sister Gertrude thinks she knows how to play and she's been slotted into the ranking list at minus three tops. It's all arranged.'

The Mother of Discipline could see no escape. Play started soon afterwards and this was an early board for the new partnership

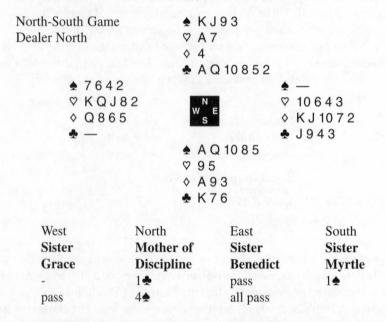

```
North-South Game          ♠ K J 9 3
Dealer North              ♡ A 7
                          ◊ 4
                          ♣ A Q 10 8 5 2
        ♠ 7 6 4 2                              ♠ —
        ♡ K Q J 8 2          N                 ♡ 10 6 4 3
        ◊ Q 8 6 5        W       E             ◊ K J 10 7 2
        ♣ —                  S                 ♣ J 9 4 3
                          ♠ A Q 10 8 5
                          ♡ 9 5
                          ◊ A 9 3
                          ♣ K 7 6
```

West	North	East	South
Sister	**Mother of**	**Sister**	**Sister**
Grace	**Discipline**	**Benedict**	**Myrtle**
-	1♣	pass	1♠
pass	4♠	all pass	

The Mother of Discipline could find no excuse for not raising her partner's suit and her call of Four Spades was passed out. The king of hearts was led and Sister Myrtle shook her head as she inspected the dummy. Five spades, six clubs, and two aces. Thirteen tricks on top! 'That's a bit good, isn't it, Reverend Mother?' she said. 'Ace, please.'

Sister Myrtle counted the tricks once more, again making the total thirteen. Nothing could go wrong, provided she remembered to draw trumps before running the club suit.

Sister Myrtle drew trumps in four rounds, then cashed the king of clubs. When West showed out, she continued with a club to the ace, then played the queen of clubs. She turned to her regular partner, Sister Benedict, in the East seat. 'Unless I've miscounted, you still have the jack of clubs, don't you?'

Sister Benedict thumbed through her hand, eventually locating the card. 'Yes, I have,' she replied.

'Just the ten, then,' said Sister Myrtle, facing her hand. 'A lucky one for us, partner. That was quite a good slam.'

The Mother of Discipline reached for the South curtain card, inspecting it in disbelief. 'You had ace-queen to five trumps, the ace of diamonds, and the king of my main suit?' she exclaimed. 'You didn't, just possibly, think you were worth another effort?'

'Not after your shut-out bid,' replied Sister Myrtle. 'If you can see your way to rebidding Three Spades, I can make one of those... what are they called... cue bids. Anyway, as it happens, the slam wasn't there.'

It was a miracle worthy of the College of Cardinals' note that the Mother of Discipline refrained from further comment. Twelve tricks had been absolutely cold, of course, simply by ruffing two diamonds. Even the way it had gone, Sister Myrtle could still have made eleven tricks by ducking the second round of clubs. The Mother of Discipline shook her head. Why did people with such limited cerebral powers play the game? Even more amazing, how had Sister Grace managed to come as high as third last year, partnering Sister Myrtle?

The Mother of Discipline surveyed her enormous partner. Sister Myrtle claimed to have tried every diet ever invented. She had spent three weeks on a cabbage soup diet. No luck. She had spent a similar period on a low-fat diet, cutting out all fried food and red meat. No success. She had tried vegetable diets, banana diets, fruit and chicken diets, pulse diets, Swiss, American, Danish diets. It was always the same story. The weight would pour off initially and all would seem to be going well. The moment she returned to her normal eating pattern, however, the pounds would simply come back on again. It was hopeless.

A round of two later the Mother Superior and the late conscript, Sister Gertrude, arrived at the table. This was the first board of the round:

Game All   ♠ K J 4 3
Dealer South   ♡ K Q 4
               ◇ 5 3
               ♣ J 9 3 2

	♠ 8		♠ Q 9 6
	♡ 8 6 2	N	♡ J 10 9 7 3
	◇ A K 10 9 6 2	W E	◇ Q
	♣ A Q 8	S	♣ 10 7 5 4

               ♠ A 10 7 5 2
               ♡ A 5
               ◇ J 8 7 4
               ♣ K 6

West	North	East	South
Sister	**Sister**	**Mother of**	**Mother**
Myrtle	**Gertrude**	**Discipline**	**Superior**
-	-	-	1♠
2◇	3♣	pass	4♠
all pass			

The Mother Superior's hand did not amount to much but she saw two reasons to advance to game. Sister Gertrude had little idea how to bid and might well put down a 14-count in the dummy. Also, the dummy might be short in diamonds.

Sister Myrtle led the ace of diamonds, noting her partner's queen, and continued with the king of diamonds, East showing out. At Trick 3 she played a third round of diamonds, hoping that partner could overruff the dummy. 'Ruff with the king, will you?' said the Mother Superior.

The jack of spades was covered by the queen and ace, the 8 falling from West. With the diamonds divided 6-1, the Mother Superior was inclined to place East with the trump length. Indeed, it seemed to her that the Principle of Restricted Choice applied. West's ♠8 was more likely to be a singleton than a chosen card from ♠98. She cashed three rounds of hearts, discarding a club from her hand, then played a low trump to the 7. All was well when West showed out and the Mother Superior could now claim ten tricks.

'Very lucky trump position for you,' grunted the Mother of Discipline. 'Swap my six with your seven and you'd have gone down.'

'You had one of the club honours?' enquired the Mother Superior.

'No, four to the 10,' replied the Mother of Discipline. 'Why do you ask?'

'Well, you've spotted it, of course,' continued the Mother Superior. 'If you ruff the king of diamonds at Trick 2, you can lead a club through my king. You take the first four tricks.'

There was a short pause. 'That was hardly with the odds when I had such good potential for a trump promotion,' declared the Mother of Discipline. 'Make my nine of trumps a small trump and I would have been there with the ruff, naturally.' She glared across the table. 'If you had the ace-queen of clubs why didn't you play a low diamond at Trick 2?' she demanded. 'My queen can only be a singleton or from the queen-jack. If you play a low diamond, I ruff and switch to a club.'

Sister Myrtle peered back uncomprehendingly. 'I did play the two of diamonds at Trick 3,' she replied. 'Didn't you see it? It was meant to be a McKenney signal to show something useful in clubs.'

'Heaven spare us!' exploded the Mother of Discipline. 'What use is a signal at Trick 3 when the key play comes at Trick 2?'

The next round saw the arrival of two nuns from the middle of the ranking list, Sister Charity and Sister Hester. 'Such a coincidence, it was, Reverend Mother,' said Sister Charity, taking her seat. 'Our positions in the ranking list put us in our regular partnership!'

The Mother of Discipline's eyes bulged. 'How on earth did I not spot that?' she exclaimed. 'That's not at all what is intended. The whole idea is that you have to do your best, playing with someone new.'

'We've done very well, Reverend Mother,' said Sister Charity. 'Everyone else has been having bidding misunderstandings against us.'

'You have an unfair advantage,' declared the Mother of Discipline. 'If you come in the masterpoints, I'll have to disqualify you.'

'That's not fair, Reverend Mother. We didn't arrange the...'

'Be silent!' cried the Mother of Discipline. She pointed to the board they were about to play and the four players drew their cards. Sister Charity sorted through an awkward-looking 13-count:

♠ K
♡ A Q J 6
♦ Q J 6 5
♣ 10 9 8 4

If she opened 1♡ and rebid one of the minors, there was every chance of ending in 2♡ on a 4-2 fit. It must be better to open 1NT, she thought. If the worst came to the worst and partner transferred into spades, at least she had the king of the suit. 'One Notrump,' said Sister Charity.

The Mother of Discipline was soon in Four Spades. This was the full deal:

```
East-West Game          ♠ A 9 7 3
Dealer West             ♡ 7 5 4
                        ◊ A 10 2
                        ♣ A J 5
        ♠ K                           ♠ J 5
        ♡ A Q J 6          N          ♡ 10 8 2
        ◊ Q J 6 5       W     E       ◊ 9 8 7 3
        ♣ 10 9 8 4         S          ♣ Q 7 6 2
                        ♠ Q 10 8 6 4 2
                        ♡ K 9 3
                        ◊ K 4
                        ♣ K 3
```

West	North	East	South
Sister	**Sister**	**Sister**	**Mother of**
Charity	**Myrtle**	**Hester**	**Discipline**
1NT	pass	pass	2♠
pass	4♠	all pass	

Sister Charity led ♣10, covered by the jack, queen and king. The Mother of Discipline inspected her trump holding. Normal play with that combination would be to cash the ace, winning when either defender held a singleton king. East had already shown up with two points, however, so West's opening bid marked her with the guarded king. The best chance must be to lead the queen, aiming to pin a singleton jack with East.

The Mother of Discipline advanced the queen of spades, covered by the king and ace. A disappointing five-spot fell from East. The Mother of Discipline now eliminated the diamond suit, followed by the clubs. These cards remained:

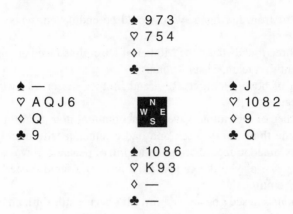

```
              ♠ 9 7 3
              ♡ 7 5 4
              ◇ —
              ♣ —
♠ —                        ♠ J
♡ A Q J 6        N         ♡ 10 8 2
◇ Q          W     E       ◇ 9
♣ 9              S         ♣ Q
              ♠ 10 8 6
              ♡ K 9 3
              ◇ —
              ♣ —
```

The Mother of Discipline tossed a trump on to the table. Facing her remaining cards in expert fashion, she leaned towards Sister Charity. 'You must lead a heart to my king or concede a ruff-and-discard,' she informed her.

'I don't think so, Reverend Mother,' replied Sister Hester. 'I have the jack of trumps over here.'

'What!' exclaimed the Mother of Discipline, hastily retrieving her cards from the table.

Sister Hester had already seen declarer's hand and knew what was required. 'Partner throws a minor-suit card, then I win and play the ten of hearts through,' she declared. 'That's one down. Very unlucky, Reverend Mother.'

The Mother of Discipline turned angrily to her left. 'You opened 1NT with a singleton?' she demanded.

'It seems to work well on this type of hand,' replied Sister Charity.

Sister Myrtle inspected the scoresheet. 'It's a mixture of 620s and 650s, Reverend Mother,' she reported. 'Another zero for us.'

Sister Hester inscribed a large and artistic 'T' in her scorecard, proceeding to hold it at arm's length to inspect her handiwork. 'Take the right view in trumps, Reverend Mother, and you can endplay my partner in diamonds,' she said. 'You know, a loser-on-loser play, throwing a heart.'

The Mother of Discipline glared at her opponent. 'Had I been informed of your unorthodox methods, I would have played it that way,' she replied. 'It's probably illegal to open 1NT with a singleton. I'll check in the English Bridge Union yellow book; we may need to adjust the score.'

It occurred to Sister Hester that ten tricks should have been made, even after misguessing the trumps. There was nothing to be lost by eliminating the clubs before the diamonds. Then, when East failed to cover ◇10, declarer could discard a heart from her hand. West would be endplayed, whoever held the trump jack.

Two or three rounds later, the Mother of Discipline faced another member of the Convent first team, Sister Thomas.

'Dull set of boards tonight, Reverend Mother,' observed Sister Thomas, taking her seat.

The Mother of Discipline gave a noncommittal nod. Sister Thomas said much the same thing every week and had a rather jaded outlook on life in general. She seemed to regard bridge as a form of penance. It was a mystery to everyone why she played the game. 'How have you fared, Sister?' asked the Mother of Discipline.

Sister Thomas raised a bushy eyebrow. 'It's been a little difficult,' she replied. 'Sister Hermione doesn't play quite the same bidding system as we do. We've played at least three laydown games in a partscore.'

The pale-faced Sister Hermione smiled weakly at the Mother of Discipline. 'I don't like to get too high,' she said.

```
Love All              ♠ 7 2
Dealer North          ♡ J 5
                      ◇ K 9 6 5 2
                      ♣ A K J 4

    ♠ K Q J 9 5                      ♠ A 10 4
    ♡ Q 10 9 4 3       N             ♡ K 8 7
    ◇ 3             W     E          ◇ 10 8 7 4
    ♣ 7 3              S             ♣ 9 8 2

                      ♠ 8 6 3
                      ♡ A 6 2
                      ◇ A Q J
                      ♣ Q 10 6 5
```

West	North	East	South
Sister	**Mother of**	**Sister**	**Sister**
Thomas	**Discipline**	**Hermione**	**Myrtle**
-	1◇	pass	2♣
2♠	3♣	pass	5♣
all pass			

Sister Thomas won the first two tricks with the king and queen of spades. Hoping to disrupt declarer's communications, she continued with a third spade at Trick 3. Sister Myrtle ruffed in the dummy and drew trumps in three rounds. All now depended on the diamond suit. She paused to check her calculations. Cash the ace and queen, then play the jack and overtake with the king. Yes! She would then be in dummy and could cash two more diamonds, throwing her heart losers.

A small defect in this plan came to light when West showed out on the second diamond. Declarer could not overtake the third diamond without setting up East's 10 and the contract went two down.

'We can't make 3NT either, without a spade stopper,' said Sister Myrtle. 'It's a better pairs score, though. It only goes one down.'

The Mother of Discipline shook her head at this absurd remark. 'Five Clubs was cold,' she declared. 'Draw two rounds of trumps, then test the diamonds. Sister Thomas shows out but she can't ruff. You cash your last diamond, then cross to dummy with a third round of trumps.'

Sister Myrtle stared back defiantly. 'I could hardly risk having one of my diamonds ruffed, she said. 'What would you have said then?'

'How's the new partnership going?' enquired a cheerful Welsh voice from behind the Mother of Discipline.

'Sister Consolata!' exclaimed the Mother of Discipline. 'I thought you were otherwise engaged, tending to Sister Euphemia.'

'She's made a splendid recovery, Reverend Mother,' replied Sister Consolata. 'We had her back in her cell by six o'clock. I could have played, actually.'

The Mother of Discipline closed her eyes, as if in pain. It made her evening of torment even worse, knowing that it had been entirely unnecessary. Why on earth hadn't Sister Consolata come straight to her study the moment she knew she would be free? Surely a modest player like her would give anything to partner an expert for a whole session.

Sister Consolata walked behind Sister Myrtle and gave her a friendly hug. 'Doing all right, then, Sister?' she enquired.

'It's strange but I usually do better with Sister Benedict,' came the reply. 'Not that it's your fault, Reverend Mother, but it's always very difficult playing in a new partnership.'

The Mother of Discipline looked wearily across the table. It was the first time she had agreed with her partner all evening.

'Quite so,' she said.

XX

Dark Times at St Hilda's

Sister Benedict was radiant. 'Isn't Christmas just the most wonderful time of the whole year?' she exclaimed. 'To think of the baby Jesus lying there in the stable, so full of peace. It's too marvellous for words.'

'You wouldn't say that if you had to get these Christmas tree lights working,' replied the sour-faced Sister Thomas. 'It's the same every time. All in perfect order when they're packed away on Twelfth Night, then they refuse to work the following year.'

Sister Beatrice put an arm around her colleague. 'I think I can help you there,' she said. 'You need to take one bulb that you know is good and, one by one, replace...'

'I know!' Sister Thomas exclaimed. 'What do you *think* I've been doing? It's not so simple when there are several broken bulbs.'

That evening, as was the tradition at St Hilda's, a Christmas Eve duplicate took place. An early round brought the Convent's four strongest players together.

Love All
Dealer West

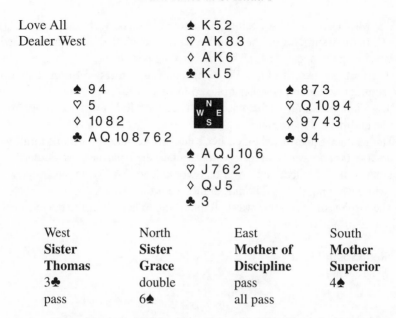

♠ K 5 2
♡ A K 8 3
◇ A K 6
♣ K J 5

♠ 9 4
♡ 5
◇ 10 8 2
♣ A Q 10 8 7 6 2

♠ 8 7 3
♡ Q 10 9 4
◇ 9 7 4 3
♣ 9 4

♠ A Q J 10 6
♡ J 7 6 2
◇ Q J 5
♣ 3

West	North	East	South
Sister	**Sister**	**Mother of**	**Mother**
Thomas	**Grace**	**Discipline**	**Superior**
3♣	double	pass	4♠
pass	6♠	all pass	

The Mother Superior arrived in Six Spades and viewed the opening lead of ♡5 with some interest. If it was a second-best lead from ♡1054 or ♡954, East's queen would fall on the second round and twelve tricks would be easy. What if the lead were a singleton, or top of a doubleton? The Mother Superior's eyes lit up. Yes, there might still be a way home. 'Ace, please, Sister,' she said.

Trumps were drawn in three rounds and the Mother Superior then led a second round of hearts towards the dummy. West discarded a club and dummy's king of hearts won the trick. Three rounds of diamonds removed Sister Thomas's holding in that suit and the Mother Superior now led a club towards the dummy.

Sister Thomas sucked in air between her teeth. If she rose with the ace, she would have to lead another club, allowing a finesse of dummy's jack. Since declarer could be counted for ten tricks outside the club suit, this would give her the contract. The only remaining chance was to play low on the club. The trick would be won in the dummy, with the king or the jack, but declarer might then be left with two heart losers.

When Sister Thomas eventually produced a low club, the Mother Superior called for dummy's king. It held the trick and she proceeded to claim the contract. 'I lead towards the jack of hearts,' she said. 'Just the twelve.'

The Mother of Discipline's eyes bulged. 'Take your ace, partner, and we beat the slam!' she exclaimed. 'In all my years I've never witnessed such a poor defence.'

The Mother Superior gasped at this intolerant display. 'Perhaps just a tad more Christmas spirit would be in order, Reverend Mother,' she reprimanded. 'However it may appear, Sister Thomas is trying her best.'

'If I took the ace of clubs, I'd be end-played,' protested Sister Thomas. 'The contract was there, whether I played the ace or not.'

'Cash it at trick one, in that case,' persisted the Mother of Discipline. 'You can't be end-played then, can you?'

The Mother Superior resumed her role as peacemaker. 'I don't think we should use that tone of voice towards a cherished partner, particularly at Christmas time,' she declared. 'You or I would lead ♣A, Reverend Mother, it goes without saying. Sister Thomas didn't see it that way.'

The Mother of Discipline was still muttering to herself as the players drew their cards for the next deal.

```
North-South Game        ♠ 8 4
Dealer South            ♡ K Q 6 3
                        ◇ 9 8 2
                        ♣ K 8 4 3
   ♠ K Q J 5                          ♠ 10 9 7 2
   ♡ 10 8 2          N                ♡ J 9 7 5 4
   ◇ Q 6 4        W      E            ◇ 10 7 5 3
   ♣ A Q 9           S                ♣ —
                        ♠ A 6 3
                        ♡ A
                        ◇ A K J
                        ♣ J 10 7 6 5 2
```

West	North	East	South
Sister	**Sister**	**Mother of**	**Mother**
Thomas	**Grace**	**Discipline**	**Superior**
-	-	-	1♣
pass	1♡	pass	2◇
pass	3♣	pass	3♠
double	4♣	pass	5♣
double	all pass		

The Mother Superior arrived in Five Clubs doubled and Sister Thomas led the king of spades, won by declarer's ace. The Mother Superior cashed the ace of hearts, then led a low trump, hoping to gain access to the heart tricks in dummy.

Once more, Sister Thomas sucked in air noisily. What was she meant to do with her ace of clubs *this* time? If she rose with the ace, in order to cash a spade trick, declarer would surely be able to pick up her trump queen. Any diamond losers could then be parked on dummy's heart honours. It must be better to play ♣9, guaranteeing herself two trump tricks. Declarer would doubtless discard her spade losers, but the queen of diamonds might then provide the setting trick.

Sister Thomas played ♣9 and the Mother Superior called for dummy's king, winning the trick. Two spades were thrown on the king-queen of hearts and declarer then ruffed a spade, eliminating that suit. Sister Thomas won the trump exit with the queen and proceeded to cash the ace of trumps. This position had been reached:

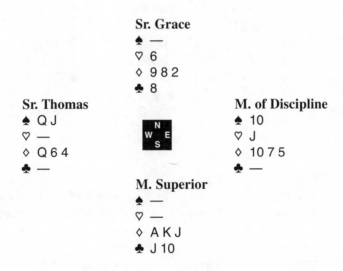

Sr. Grace
♠ —
♡ 6
♢ 9 8 2
♣ 8

Sr. Thomas
♠ Q J
♡ —
♢ Q 6 4
♣ —

M. of Discipline
♠ 10
♡ J
♢ 10 7 5
♣ —

M. Superior
♠ —
♡ —
♢ A K J
♣ J 10

Sister Thomas had no good card to play. Since a spade would clearly give a useful ruff-and-discard, she had to try her luck with a low diamond. The Mother Superior spread her remaining cards face-up on the table. 'I make the rest,' she announced.

The Mother of Discipline slumped in her chair. 'What a foolish double, partner!' she exclaimed. 'Did you think that minus 750 would be a good board for us?'

'It was a cost-nothing double, Reverend Mother,' Sister Thomas replied. 'Losing 600 would be a bottom anyway, so I might as well double and hope for the magic plus 200.'

'Rubbish!' cried the Mother of Discipline. 'Even an ailing octagenarian such as myself can recognise a poor double when she sees one.'

Several pairs of young eyes were trained on the action, the young novices at adjacent tables lapping up every word. The Mother Superior waved an imperious hand in their direction, indicating that they should avert their eyes. 'I'm sure we can set a better example to the younger Sisters than that,' she said, with an admonishing glance at the Mother of Discipline. 'Particularly at this time of year.'

This was the final board of the round:

```
Game All              ♠ 9 6 5
Dealer South          ♡ A 8 2
                      ◇ K Q 6 3
                      ♣ J 8 5
     ♠ K Q J 8 2                      ♠ 10 7 3
     ♡ 9 4             N              ♡ 10 7 5
     ◇ 10 4         W     E           ◇ 9 8 5 2
     ♣ K Q 7 2         S              ♣ 10 9 6
                      ♠ A 4
                      ♡ K Q J 6 3
                      ◇ A J 7
                      ♣ A 4 3
```

West	North	East	South
Sister	**Sister**	**Mother of**	**Mother**
Thomas	**Grace**	**Discipline**	**Superior**
-	-	-	1♡
1♠	2♠	pass	3♠
pass	4♡	pass	6♡
all pass			

Sister Thomas led the king of spades and down went the dummy.

The Mother Superior was unimpressed by what she saw. 'I was expecting rather more than that after your cue-bid,' she said.

'It only shows a sound raise to the three-level, Reverend Mother,' replied Sister Grace.

The Mother Superior said no more, reluctant as always to criticise her partner's bidding. Since when did a 9-loser hand with three trumps count as any sort of raise to the three-level, though? A raise to 2♡ would have been plenty on that hand. Now, how on earth could she make twelve tricks?

'Shall we get on?' said Sister Thomas. At this rate, time would run out and the Director would scrap the board. That wasn't at all what she wanted, with an out-and-out top in prospect.

The Mother Superior won the spade lead with the ace and drew two rounds of trumps with the king and the queen. Hoping for the best, she then played four rounds of diamonds. Luck was with her when West held only two diamonds but was unable to ruff. The Mother Superior discarded her spade loser, then ruffed a spade in her hand. These cards were still to be played:

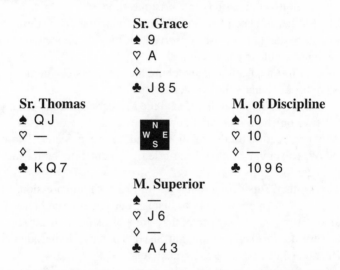

Sr. Grace
♠ 9
♡ A
♢ —
♣ J 8 5

Sr. Thomas
♠ Q J
♡ —
♢ —
♣ K Q 7

M. of Discipline
♠ 10
♡ 10
♢ —
♣ 10 9 6

M. Superior
♠ —
♡ J 6
♢ —
♣ A 4 3

The Mother Superior led her penultimate trump and – for the third hand in succession – a strange sucking noise arose from a Westerly direction. If Sister Thomas threw a club, it would be a simple matter for declarer to continue with ace and another club, setting up dummy's jack for a twelfth trick. She therefore discarded the jack of spades, dummy's trump ace winning the trick. 'Play the spade, will you?' instructed the Mother Superior.

Dummy's last spade was ruffed with the jack and all four hands were now down to clubs. Murmuring a small prayer, the Mother Superior led a low club towards the dummy. Sister Thomas could see that the defence would at an end if she played an honour. Hoping that declarer held ♣9, and might then try her luck with dummy's ♣8, she contributed a cool ♣7. The Mother Superior did not possess the club nine and therefore had no guess in the suit. 'Jack, please,' she said. The card held the trick and the slam had been made.

The Mother Superior was exultant. 'I don't believe I've ever seen three such splendid hands back-to-back!' she exclaimed. 'We can count ourselves blessed indeed to have such a Christmas gift bestowed upon us.'

The Mother of Discipline felt unable to include herself in this assessment. Three zeroes running, when she hadn't made a single mistake? That sort of present, she could do without.

Another matter occurring to her, the Mother Superior turned towards Sister Thomas. 'I see that the Christmas tree lights have not been switched on yet,' she said. 'We are not the wealthiest of orders, it's true, but I think we can justify a few extra units of electricity at Christmas time.'

The Mother of Discipline nodded her agreement. 'They throw quite a light on the crib beside the tree,' she observed. 'If they're not switched on, the baby Jesus won't be able to see anything.'

'It's not just a question of switching them on,' Sister Thomas replied. 'The lights are broken, that's the problem.'

'I think I can help you there,' said the Mother Superior. 'What you need to do is to take one bulb that you know is good and...'

A world record intake of air flowed between Sister Thomas's teeth. 'I KNOW, Reverend Mother!' she cried. 'I spent four hours this afternoon, trying to get the lights to work.'

The Mother Superior adopted her most beatific expression. 'These trials are sent to us as an opportunity to display our patience and cheerfulness,' she declared. 'However, it may seem, they are a blessing in disguise.'

A very heavy disguise, thought Sister Thomas. Some other Sister could take advantage of such a blessing next year.

'Move for the next round!' called a voice from across the room.

'I feel sure the tree will be shining brightly by the time the Sisters awake on Christmas morning,' said the Mother Superior, rising to her feet. 'You still have seven hours available, Sister Thomas, and we all have the greatest faith in you!'